"Being an educator, coach, and parent that has lost a child to suicide, I truly believe that a comprehensive program such as Lifelines has the potential to help educate all those involved. If through this program we save one child's life and the pain and grief associated with this journey, it is educational time well spent."

CRAIG MILES, 30-YEAR EDUCATOR, COACH, SPEAKER

"My son's 13-year-old friends knew he was contemplating suicide but did not know how to appropriately respond to this crisis. There was no suicide prevention education program at his Vermont school. Our young people are on the frontlines every day; they are typically the first potential responders for a peer at risk for suicide. It has always made sense that education is our best tool to ensure that first response was appropriate. Lifelines: A Suicide Prevention Program is by far the most comprehensive, evidence-based program I have come across."

JOHN HALLIGAN, MOTIVATIONAL SPEAKER, WWW.RYANSSTORY.ORG

Lifelines

A Suicide Prevention Program

Maureen Underwood, L.C.S.W.
John Kalafat, Ph.D.

The Maine Youth Suicide Prevention Program,
Led by the Maine CDC

HAZELDEN®

Hazelden
Center City, Minnesota 55012
hazelden.org

ISBN: 978-1-59285-747-0

Notice and Disclaimer

This curriculum is for educational and informational purposes only and should not be considered, or used as a substitute for, professional medical/psychological advice, diagnosis, and treatment. Hazelden makes no warranty, guarantee, or promise, express or implied, regarding the effectiveness of this curriculum in the prevention of suicide in specific situations. Hazelden does not take responsibility for any loss, injury, or damage caused by using the curriculum information and in no event shall Hazelden, its employees, or its contractors or agents be liable for any special indirect or consequential damages or any loss or damages whatsoever resulting from injury, loss of income or profits, whether in an action of contract, negligence, or other tortious action, arising in connection with the use or performance of any information contained in the curriculum or associated materials. Hazelden does not monitor and is not responsible for statements made by instructors or others, or for the quality of instruction provided in conjunction with this curriculum.

13 12 11 10 09   1 2 3 4 5 6

Cover design by David Spohn
Interior design and typesetting by Percolator

Contents

ix Acknowledgments
xi How to Use the CD-ROM

1   Introduction to *Lifelines*

11 Introduction to Teen Suicide

19 Part 1: Administrative Readiness Consultation

53 Part 2: Training for School Faculty and Staff

71 Part 3: Parent Workshop

81 Part 4: Student Curriculum

    89   Session 1: When Is a Friend in Trouble?
    101 Session 2: How Do I Help a Friend?
    109 Session 3: Where Can I Go to Get Help?
    119 Session 4: How Can I Use What I've Learned?

124 Notes
127 School-based Suicide Prevention Resources
130 About the Authors

For My Colleague, John Kalafat

When the *Lifelines* program was first conceived, it was the early 1980s and the rates of youth suicide had tripled in the preceding thirty years. School-based programs to address what was considered to be a public health epidemic were virtually non-existent. John Kalafat and I were colleagues at a community mental health center in a suburban New Jersey town when we were asked by the director of guidance at a local high school to develop a curriculum about suicide prevention for students.

Our community backgrounds—I am a social worker and John was a community psychologist—helped us understand the need to translate the mental health concepts of suicide awareness and prevention into practical, easily understood lessons. We believed the curriculum needed to fit into the regular school schedule and be taught by faculty members to reinforce for students that they could find approachable, helpful adults within the school.

Our mutual appreciation for the importance of systemic program commitment led to the development of program components for all levels of the school community, from administrators to faculty and staff, students, and parents. The program was piloted, tested, and revised numerous times. In 2000, John became a project consultant for the Maine Youth Suicide Prevention Program and *Lifelines* was implemented in a number of Maine schools.

The field of youth suicide prevention has grown slowly and cautiously since those early years. It has finally reached a point where evaluation data on school-based programs have demonstrated that well-constructed, school-based programs can be effective tools in youth suicide awareness. And John Kalafat was one of the field's pioneers and preeminent leaders.

John died suddenly in October 2007. With his colleagues in Maine, he had just completed the process of submitting the final *Lifelines* evaluation data to the National Registry of Evidence-based Programs and Practices (NREPP) for evidence-based practice review, and he and I were working together on the manuscript for this publication.

While his loss is certainly profound for me on both a personal and professional level, it is an even greater loss for the field of youth suicide prevention. John had a passionate and career-long commitment to the implementation and evaluation of school-based prevention programs. He was a pragmatist who understood that successful, effective program development took time; and he championed the need for programs to set appropriate goals and be carefully evaluated. He understood the importance of programmatic continuity and insisted on providing training to ensure program fidelity and on developing strategies for program maintenance.

Yet despite his extraordinary level of academic and intellectual sophistication, John was a consummate egalitarian. He nurtured collaborative relationships with colleagues from all mental health disciplines as well as from program consumers— teachers, school staff members, and students, whose contributions he genuinely valued equally. In the *Lifelines* curriculum, for example, he was most moved by the young boys whose help-seeking interventions for a friend are described in one of the curriculum's videos. "These kids are the real heroes in suicide prevention," he often said.

Those who worked with John miss his intellect, compassion, wit, and contagious sense of curiosity about the world around him. Those who are fortunate enough to be exposed to the work he left behind will be impressed by his thoroughness, intellectual rigor, and obvious commitment to evaluated interventions that effectively address identified suicide prevention needs.

John's legacy to youth suicide prevention lives on in the *Lifelines* program. As you implement this program in your school, I have no doubt that you will share John's observations that your students are the real heroes in suicide prevention.

But in my mind's eye, John Kalafat was one of its real heroes, too.

—*Maureen M. Underwood*

Acknowledgments

From start to finish, *Lifelines* has been inspired by the scores of dedicated mental health professionals and school staff members who shared our belief in the critical importance of youth suicide prevention.

John Kalafat and I were especially fortunate to have had the vision and insight of Cas Jakubic, Ph.D. (whose request for a school-based suicide prevention program in 1980 spawned the original *Lifelines* curriculum), the support and encouragement of Dennis Lafer, New Jersey Deputy Director of Mental Health Services, and the wisdom of Diane Ryerson, LCSW, who provided input on revisions to early versions of the program. Also, a big thank you to Sue O'Halloran for her work on the student curriculum.

The enthusiasm of our Hazelden editors, Pamela Foster and Sue Thomas, helped guide the *Lifelines* curriculum to another level of professionalism. Special thanks to Nicole Messinger Post for the leadership, sensitivity, and understanding she brought to the video shoot. Sharon Shepherd-Levine and Bob Griffiths also added their sensitive and creative vision to aspects of the video production and Anne Damianos-Kalafat's perseverance and determination steadied the project at difficult and critical junctures.

The ultimate champions of *Lifelines*, though, have always been the survivor parents, whose passionate commitment to youth suicide prevention inspired and motivated us. Special gratitude to Barb Barisonek, Scott Fritz, and Don Quigley for sharing their stories, courage, and strength of spirit.

How to Use the CD-ROM

This manual comes with a CD-ROM that contains downloadable and printable resources for administrators, school faculty and staff, parents, and students, including all the handouts needed for implementing *Lifelines*. Many of the resources are in PDF format and can be accessed using Adobe Reader. If you do not have Adobe Reader, you can download it for free at www.adobe.com. A few of the documents are in Microsoft PowerPoint. If you do not have Microsoft PowerPoint, you can download a free version of PowerPoint Viewer at www.microsoft.com.

Whenever you see this icon in the manual, this means the resource needed is located on the CD-ROM. There will be a number next to the icon that corresponds to the number of the document on the CD-ROM. An SP symbol (SP) near the icon indicates that a Spanish version of the document is also available on the CD-ROM.

To access the resources on the CD-ROM, put the disc in your computer's CD-ROM player. Open your version of Adobe Reader or Microsoft PowerPoint, and then open the documents by clicking on the ones you wish to use. These resources cannot be modified, but they can be printed for use without concern for copyright infringement. For a list of what is contained on the CD-ROM, see the *Read Me First* document on the CD-ROM.

Introduction to Lifelines

WHAT IS *LIFELINES?*

Lifelines: A Suicide Prevention Program is a comprehensive suicide prevention program that targets the entire school community, providing suicide awareness material for administrators, faculty and staff, parents, and students. It is an outgrowth of programs initially developed by the authors in the 1980s in response to requests from schools for help in dealing with an increase in suicidal behavior among students. While *Lifelines* provides basic information about youth suicide, it is primarily directed at helping everyone in the school community recognize when a student is at potential risk of suicide and understand how and where to access help.

The objectives of *Lifelines* are to increase the likelihood that

- members of the school community can more readily identify potentially suicidal adolescents, know how to initially respond to them, and know how to rapidly obtain help for them

- troubled adolescents are aware of and have immediate access to helping resources and seek such help as an alternative to suicidal actions

WHAT ARE THE *LIFELINES* PROGRAM COMPONENTS?

Lifelines consists of four components that are considered essential to a comprehensive school-based approach to adolescent suicide prevention. These components are (1) administrative readiness consultation, (2) training for school faculty and staff, (3) parent workshop, and (4) student curriculum. Handouts and additional resources on the CD-ROM supplement these components.

1

Administrative Readiness Consultation

This component outlines the school's prepared and planned response to suicide prevention. Setting policies and procedures demonstrates administrative commitment and support for the school's suicide prevention activities, and provides the guidelines for crisis response to students at risk for suicide or in the event of a death by suicide.

Training for School Faculty and Staff

Generally designed as an in-service workshop, this component provides the basic information about adolescent suicide that has the most practical implications for school personnel, outlines the critical but limited role of faculty and staff in identifying and responding to suicidal behavior, and identifies in-school referral resources. The role of faculty and staff in suicide prevention is described in this presentation using three goals:

1. Learning the warning signs of suicide

2. Identifying at-risk students

3. Referring at-risk students to appropriate resources

Parent Workshop

This presentation for parents reviews basic information about adolescent suicide and provides an overview of the school's response program, as well as brief guidelines for parental response to suicidal behavior. Resources for additional information on suicide and community support services are also provided.

Student Curriculum

This component cannot be implemented until the first three components have been completed. It would be inappropriate to train students to identify and refer potentially at-risk peers if the adults in the school or at home are unprepared to respond to these referrals.

The student curriculum is a four-session unit usually taught in eighth-, ninth-, or tenth-grade health classes. The curriculum includes detailed lesson plans that cover facts about suicide and the students' role in suicide prevention. The curriculum also reviews in-school and community resources and is designed to be taught by a school faculty member.

The four sessions teach students

- relevant facts about suicide, including warning signs

- how to recognize the threat of suicidal thoughts and behavior and to take troubled peers seriously

- how to respond to troubled peers

- to demonstrate positive attitudes about intervention and help-seeking behaviors

- to identify resources, be able to name one helpful adult, and know how resources will respond

Two videos are included in the student curriculum:

- *A Teen's Guide to Suicide Prevention:* Students watch and discuss this video during session 2. The video shows several scenarios about how teens can recognize the warning signs of suicide in their peers. Each scenario features role-plays showing students how to respond and how to get help for a peer who may be thinking about suicide.

- *One Life Saved: The Story of a Suicide Intervention:* Students watch and discuss this video during session 3. The video documents a true story of a suicide intervention that occurred after three students watched *A Teen's Guide to Suicide Prevention* and completed the *Lifelines* curriculum. The students credit the video with showing them how to recognize the warning signs in their peer, and how they got help for this peer and possibly saved his life.

IS *LIFELINES* A RESEARCH-BASED PROGRAM?

Lifelines is a research-based program. It has been identified as a promising program by the Suicide Prevention Resource Center (SPRC) and has been submitted to be included in the National Registry of Evidence-based Programs and Practices (NREPP). One of the first school-based suicide prevention programs in the country, it has been adapted and changed to reflect both program evaluation and increases in knowledge about youth attitudes toward seeking help.

Lifelines content is grounded in several areas of research related to adolescent suicide prevention. It reflects research that has determined that most suicidal youths confide their concerns more often to peers than to adults, and that some adolescents, particularly males, do not respond to troubled peers in empathic or helpful ways. It also addresses the fact that as few as 25 percent of peer confidants tell an adult about a troubled or suicidal peer, and that school-based adults are often adolescents' last choice as confidants for personal concerns.

Lifelines also incorporates the evidence that getting help from their peers is beneficial for youths. Participation in helping interactions can shape positive social behaviors and also reduce problematic behavior. Finally, the curriculum incorporates research that has shown that a major factor that buffers youths in stressful situations is a sense of connection and contribution to their school or community.

Lifelines was the subject of extensive research during 2005 in twelve public schools in Maine. This outcome evaluation demonstrates that the curriculum promotes increases in students' knowledge about suicide and resources, as well as expressed intent to intervene on behalf of at-risk peers. Findings also support teacher acceptance of the program and increased student confidence in the school's ability to respond to at-risk youth.

For more information on the research behind *Lifelines*, consult the journal articles and book chapters listed in the endnotes on page 124.[1]

HOW IS *LIFELINES* DIFFERENT FROM OTHER SUICIDE PREVENTION PROGRAMS?

To put *Lifelines* into context, it's important to understand the different types of school-based suicide prevention programs. They can fall into one of three categories:

1. Universal interventions, which are directed at an entire population such as a school or a grade level

2. Selective interventions, which focus on subpopulations sharing certain risk factors such as students who have been treated for substance abuse

3. Indicated interventions, which target specific individuals who have been identified as being at risk such as students who have reported making suicide attempts

Like most school-based programs, *Lifelines* is a universal program. Besides being strongly research based, even in the field of universal programs it is unique in several ways:

- It is a *comprehensive* universal program, with specific, detailed content for all four school-community components. Many other programs target only one or two community components.

- Program content presents information in language that is accurate and easily understandable.

- *Lifelines* is designed to strengthen internal school resources by training teachers to present the student curriculum instead of using outside resources.

- Student sessions, which are 45 minutes long, fit easily into class periods and content is aligned with national curriculum standards.

- The curriculum, in its consistency with school mandates and culture, is not designed with a primary focus on mental health. *Lifelines* does not aim to screen students for suicide risk or address suicidal feelings or behaviors. Instead, sessions emphasize help-seeking behaviors and are aimed at students who come in contact with at-risk peers.

HOW IS *LIFELINES* IMPLEMENTED IN A SCHOOL OR NON-SCHOOL SETTING?

The implementation of *Lifelines* begins with an assessment of school policies and procedures by administrators during the administrative readiness consultation. When schools already have such procedures in place, this initial meeting simply reviews school protocol and encourages the involvement of local community mental health providers in the school's response program. If schools do not have these policies, consultation is directed at helping them establish guidelines that are in line with nationally recommended standards.

This consultation also identifies the in-school resources to which students identified as at potential risk for suicide will be referred. Because the *Lifelines* program is designed to increase awareness about suicide risk, it is essential that these staff members be prepared to effectively manage referrals, which often increase as a result of program information about suicide risk. (See Guidelines for Making Effective Referrals on the CD-ROM.) Resources that enhance staff competence by reviewing current protocols for assessment and management of at-risk youth in the school setting are available.

INTRO-1

After this review of administrative polices and procedures, a faculty and staff training is arranged. This presentation, which usually lasts 45 minutes to an hour, can take place in a variety of formats and is structured to emphasize information that has practical implications for educators. It also serves to officially introduce the *Lifelines* program to the school community and explain the critical but limited role faculty and staff play in its successful implementation.

The third aspect of implementation is the parent workshop, which reviews the *Lifelines* curriculum, provides general suicide prevention information, and outlines strategies to help parents address suicide prevention with their teens. Community mental health resources are also reviewed.

The final component and core of the program is the student curriculum. While the material is developmentally appropriate for eighth through twelfth grades, it is best suited for eighth, ninth, or tenth grade. School teachers or staff who have been designated as instructors will receive training to deliver the four student sessions. This training ensures instructors' comfort with the material as well as fidelity in curriculum implementation.

Components of *Lifelines* can be used in non-school settings. The faculty and staff presentation can be adapted for use with caregivers in any youth-based organization, such as Boy Scouts or Girl Scouts, or in faith-based youth groups. It has also been delivered at meetings of school principals and other school administrative personnel as part of a general community education process, or as part of an effort to inform school personnel of the need for and the availability of comprehensive suicide education programs.

The student curriculum can also be used with youth in community groups and organizations. The caveat with such youth adaptations, however, is that curriculum activities have not been independently evaluated for either impact or effectiveness.

WHAT RESOURCES ARE AVAILABLE TO HELP WITH THIS TOPIC?

It is a good idea to enlist the support of local community mental health resources in your school's suicide prevention activities. Many agencies offer pamphlets and brochures on suicide prevention that could be distributed to your faculty and parents. Many states have developed a state suicide prevention plan. Some state plans are more comprehensive than others, but it's worth taking a look at your state's plan to see if it offers any youth suicide resources. The list of state plans can be found on the home page for the Suicide Prevention Resource Center at www.sprc.org. The Web site lists a variety of other helpful resources and is updated regularly.

A second organization that has an exceptionally helpful Web site is the American Foundation for Suicide Prevention (www.afsp.org). AFSP is the leading national not-for-profit organization exclusively dedicated to understanding and preventing suicide through research and education. AFSP has more than thirty chapters across the country and is especially valuable for locating support groups for people who have experienced the suicide of a family member or friend.

The Society for the Prevention of Teen Suicide provides a training program for school staff on its Web site (www.sptsnj.org) that has been designated as a "best practice." This site includes downloadable PDF files for teachers, parents, and students, as well as a manual for postvention, which is response in the aftermath of a suicide. It also includes regularly updated links to useful youth suicide prevention Web sites worldwide.

School staff members such as psychologists, social workers, nurses, or child study team members who are responsible for making initial assessments of students suspected of being at risk for suicide will find the Web site of the American Association of Suicidology (www.suicidology.org) particularly helpful. This organization is a leader in the advancement of scientific and programmatic efforts in suicide prevention through research, education, and training. It offers a school suicide prevention accreditation program designed to increase the competence and confidence of school staff in their interventions with students at risk for suicide.

The Maine Youth Suicide Prevention Program has an array of resource material and information for adults as well as a separate Web site designed with youth for youth. Visit www.maine.gov/suicide and www.maine.gov/suicide/youth/.

CAVEATS TO CONSIDER

Although an attempt has been made to render *Lifelines* as complete as possible, a number of caveats must be considered when implementing this program.

1. Training is important. While *Lifelines* is a detailed, field-tested, and comprehensive package, it is not meant for use by inexperienced community consultants or school personnel. That is, *Lifelines* is best carried out through collaboration between consultants who have solid experience in community consultation, systems entry, and mental health/health education and school personnel who have experience in, or are willing to learn, the provision of sensitive health education and rapid response programs.

2. Teaching about suicide must be voluntary. While *Lifelines* is based on the premise that regular school teachers can teach the material, providing education on suicide must be done on a voluntary basis. Certain teachers may decide to opt out or be excused by administration from teaching this material for a variety of reasons.

3. The teacher is the *most* important piece. These materials have been carefully screened and field-tested. However, no materials are as important as the person delivering them. Teachers covering this material need special preparation. In addition to the *Lifelines* teacher training, teachers who present this material to students must take the time to read the additional resources on teen suicide listed in this manual on pages 127–129, and become thoroughly familiar with school resources and procedures. The many schools that have used *Lifelines* have found that teachers who teach these sessions are looked at by students as resources and are more likely to be approached about this topic. In order to respond to inquiries that arise during the sessions and outside of class, this extra preparation is necessary.

The best *Lifelines* teachers are those who

- have rapport with students in and outside of the classroom
- *want* to teach the program as opposed to being forced to teach it
- are sufficiently comfortable in talking about suicide openly and honestly
- are able to link a suicidal student to help

4. The classroom sessions are designed to be presented in four 45-minute or two 90-minute class periods. However, they are flexible and more time can be used, particularly to accommodate discussions of students' current issues and feelings. Experienced teachers know that it is important to take the time to respond to and fully discuss issues that come up in a given class. The first time through may take longer.

5. Substitute material carefully. After some experience, teachers may want to substitute their own material for different parts of the curriculum. However, care must be taken to maintain active participation (e.g., don't substitute a lecture for an exercise). Alternate exercises should be tested first to check for unanticipated effects, and media must be carefully chosen. Media and exercises should promote help-seeking behavior. *There is no place in* Lifelines *for media depicting suicidal acts or featuring previous attempters.*

6. The classroom lessons cannot stand alone. Schools can implement the administrative readiness consultation, faculty and staff training, and parent workshop without teaching the curriculum, but they should *never* implement the curriculum without these other components having been carried out first. Also, it is important to be aware that classroom material on problem solving, self-esteem, communication skills, substance abuse, sex education, interpersonal violence, and other health topics can supplement and enhance the impact of *Lifelines*.

7. Be sensitive to those who may have attempted or lost a loved one to suicide. While these lessons have a low-key, educational focus, they do generate discussion about suicide. Such discussion might be upsetting to students who have made a non-lethal attempt, those who have been identified as at risk, or those who have experienced the suicide attempt or death of a friend or family member. Such students should be approached prior to the class, informed of the topic, and provided the option of not attending. When this is done, the student often both chooses to attend and actively participates. Of course, as with any subject matter that may touch on students' personal lives, the teacher must be sensitive to student reactions and follow up after the class with any students who appear to have been distressed by program content.

8. What if? If a school has recently experienced a death from suicide, the program should not be started for at least a semester while postvention procedures are carried out. If a suicide death occurs while the curriculum is in place, the regular *Lifelines* sessions should be suspended for at least a semester in favor of postvention procedures. *Good postvention practices contribute greatly to suicide prevention.*

As this rather long list of caveats indicates, providing an effective response to suicide is a complex endeavor. As we, the program developers, learn more about this process, we expect to make further modifications in our approach; and, as we have in the past, we welcome continued feedback from those who use the *Lifelines* program. Finally, probably more than any other community education program that we have developed, we sincerely hope that the need for programs such as *Lifelines* soon passes.

Introduction to Teen Suicide

The following is based on a true story.

Nicole and Tanya had been friends with Kate since fourth grade. By the time they were in eighth grade their friendship circle had widened, but they still sat together at lunch and shared shopping trips and sleepovers. That was until about six months ago, when Kate started to act differently.

The girls noticed that she cancelled weekend plans suddenly, with excuses that seemed pretty lame. When they questioned her about it, Kate would shrug her shoulders and say she was just tired. She was quiet at lunch, barely eating, and generally looked around distractedly rather than joining in the conversation.

Her grades still seemed good, but she wasn't as enthusiastic about class assignments and she stopped offering to help her friends with projects the way she had before.

Nicole and Tanya were concerned. They decided they would ask Kate if they had done anything to make her mad at them, but when they approached her she apologized for not being a good friend and told them she felt like they might be better off without her. She was bored with everything, she said, and wasn't sure she would ever feel better. The girls responded with assurances that Kate was still a great friend. They suggested a plan to go to a new movie they all had been looking forward to seeing, and Kate agreed to go with them.

Early on the day of their scheduled movie outing, Nicole got a text from Kate saying she couldn't go. When Nicole asked why, Kate simply said "goodbye" and signed off.

Duplicating this page is illegal. Do not copy this material without written permission from the publisher.

Nicole and Tanya were frustrated with Kate so they went to the movie without her. When she didn't show up for school the following Monday, they became concerned. Nicole's mom called Kate's mom who told her that Kate had taken an overdose of Tylenol and was in the local hospital. She was okay physically but would need psychiatric treatment for what Kate admitted had been a suicide attempt.

For many students like Nicole, Tanya, and Kate, suicide is not something that happens to other people—they are extremely familiar with its unfortunate reality, even in middle school.

So, how prevalent is teen suicide? Consider the following national statistics[1]:

- In the United States, suicide is the third-leading cause of death for fifteen- to twenty-four-year-olds, following accidents and homicides.

- One in six high school students has thoughts about suicide.

- 16.9 percent of high school students have made a suicide plan in the past twelve months.

- One in eleven high school students has made an attempt in the past twelve months.

- The suicide attempt rate has increased most dramatically for ten- to fourteen-year-olds.

- Of school psychologists surveyed, 86 percent have counseled a student who has threatened or attempted suicide.

- Of those psychologists, 62 percent have had a student make a nonfatal attempt at school.

- Of those psychologists, 35 percent have had a student in their school die by suicide, and more than half of them reported more than one death.

HOW DOES TEEN SUICIDE AFFECT STUDENTS, SCHOOLS, AND COMMUNITIES?

No one whose life has been touched by a teen suicide has to read these stunning statistics to understand the impact of a self-inflicted death. But the scope of these numbers really doesn't matter when you are confronted by the name and the face of a child who has died by his or her own hand. As anyone who has had experience with youth suicide will tell you, the impact is devastating.

The troubling question that is always in the forefront of everyone's mind can be summed up in one word: Why? It is often followed by what is called "an exaggerated sense of responsibility"—the feeling that something could have personally been done to prevent the death. Even young children struggle to understand why the suicide took place, and often adopt simplistic reasoning to address their feelings of guilt. For example, a church youth group of twelve-year-olds responded to the suicide of a peer by deciding that the boy had died because the group had made fun of his clothes. They reasoned that if they hadn't teased him, he would still be alive today.

Parents, schools, and communities experience the same painful search for reasons, which are always impossible to figure out and to comprehend. What could ever have been so bad that it would lead a teen to suicide? And what can be done to make sure it never happens again?

This last question is a major concern for school communities because research tells us that there is a risk that adolescents will imitate suicidal behavior. Teens copy each other in so many superficial ways, and, unfortunately, they copy suicidal behavior as well.

WHY SHOULD SCHOOLS ADDRESS THE ISSUE OF TEEN SUICIDE?

These troubling statistics tell us that at any given time, over 14.5 percent of our high school students are having thoughts about suicide and about 7 percent have actually made a suicide attempt in the last twelve months.[2] While we may not know exactly who they are, these students are sitting in our classrooms. And although there may be a lot about suicide that we don't understand, what we can say for sure is that students who are thinking about dying are not concentrating on academic studies.

As stated by the Carnegie Task Force on Education, "School systems are not responsible for meeting every need of their students, but when the need directly affects learning, the school must meet the challenge."[3] By addressing teen suicide in a focused but comprehensive way, a school system can meet this challenge without overstepping its boundaries and becoming a mental health clinic. It can stand as a resource to potentially at-risk students by letting them know that the entire school community takes the problem of suicide seriously and has committed staff time and resources to addressing suicidal behavior.

DO SCHOOL PROGRAMS REALLY HAVE AN IMPACT?

School-based suicide prevention programs for students began in the 1980s. These programs tried to "normalize" suicide as a stress response as a way to encourage student discussion. Unfortunately, the programs gave the impression that feeling suicidal was a normal response to stress. Follow-up studies indicated that some of these programs achieved modest gains in student knowledge and positive attitudes toward help-seeking for suicide, while others had no effect or actually received negative student response. In light of the limitations of these early programs, emphasis shifted toward programs that emphasized skills training (including improvement of student coping skills), the education of school personnel, and in-screening students for risk through self-report and individual interviews.

Evaluation studies of contemporary programs have shown them to be mostly well received and sustainable. Controlled studies show knowledge gains, improved attitudes toward help-seeking behavior, actual increases in help-seeking, and decreases in self-reported suicide attempts.

There is also evidence that certain programs are not effective.[4] One-time programs, such as assemblies, do not provide enough exposure to the messages of suicide prevention, nor do they allow for monitoring of student reactions. Programs that use media depictions of suicidal behaviors or speeches by teens who have made suicide attempts should not be used, as they could have modeling effects for at-risk teens.

CAN TALKING ABOUT SUICIDE IN A SCHOOL CAUSE MORE SUICIDE?

Absolutely not! There are four main arguments in response to the myth that talking with kids about suicide will "plant" the idea:

1. Students are already well aware of suicide from their experience with suicidal peers and the media.[5]

2. In the authors' thirty years of hotline experience and twenty years of school-based suicide prevention programming, there has never been a case of planting the idea. The facts in regard to stimulation of suicidal behavior are best summarized by the following quotes from the Centers for Disease Control and Prevention: "There is no evidence of increased suicidal ideation or behavior among program participants"[6] and "Furthermore, numerous research and intervention efforts have been completed without any reports of harm."[7]

3. Several evaluations of school-based programs show increased likelihood that program participants will tell an adult about a suicidal peer as opposed to keeping that information to themselves.[8]

4. Two long-term follow-up studies in counties where suicide prevention programs were provided show reductions in youth suicide rates in the county, while state rates remained unchanged or increased for the same period of time.[9]

Remember, educational programs are not aimed at suicidal feelings per se, but instead emphasize knowing the warning signs, taking action, and obtaining help.

WHAT ARE THE RISK FACTORS AND WARNING SIGNS OF TEEN SUICIDE?

While the causes of youth suicide are complex and determined by many factors, mental health professionals have learned some things about the population of students who may be at increased risk for suicide. Current knowledge about the risk factors and warning signs of teen suicide comes from clinical sources and "psychological autopsy" studies of youth who have completed suicide. Researchers interview the family members, friends, school staff, and other significant people who knew the deceased and try to discover the factors that may have contributed to the death.

Let's look first at what we have learned from these clinical studies and then translate this information into a formula that might be useful in a school setting:

- The vast majority of youth who died by suicide had significant psychiatric problems, including depression, conduct disorders, and substance abuse problems.[10]

- Between one-quarter to one-third had made a prior attempt.[11]

- A family history of suicide greatly increased the risk.[12]

- Stressful life events such as interpersonal losses, legal or disciplinary crises, or changes for which the teen felt unprepared to cope were also reported.[13]

Teens who are suicidal don't just wake up one day and decide that life is no longer worth living; complex dynamics underlie suicide attempts and completions. These dynamics provide an important foundation for our understanding of suicidal youth, but this information may not be accessible or even relevant in a school setting. What is more relevant to those in a school are the "warning signs" of suicide. These warning signs are attitudes or behaviors that *can be* observed when a student may be at risk for suicide. The *Lifelines* program organizes these warning signs with the acrostic FACTS, which stands for feelings, actions, changes, threats, and situations.

Feelings

- Hopelessness—feeling like things are bad and won't get any better
- Fear of losing control, going crazy, harming oneself or others
- Helplessness—a belief that there's nothing that can make life better
- Worthlessness—feeling useless and of no value
- Self-hate, guilt, or shame
- Extreme sadness or loneliness
- Anxiety or worry

Actions

- Drug or alcohol abuse
- Talking or writing about death or destruction
- Aggression
- Recklessness

Changes

- Personality—behaving like a different person, becoming withdrawn, feeling tired all the time, not caring about anything, or becoming more talkative or outgoing
- Behavior—inability to concentrate
- Sleeping pattern—sleeping all the time or not being able to sleep
- Eating habits—loss of appetite and/or overeating
- Losing interest in friends, hobbies, personal appearance
- Sudden improvement after a period of being down or withdrawn

Threats

- Statements like "How long does it take to bleed to death?"
- Threats like "I won't be around much longer" or "You'd be better off without me"

- Making plans, such as studying about ways to die or obtaining the means to self-inflict injury or death

- Suicide attempts

Situations

- Getting into trouble at school, at home, or with the law

- Recent losses

- Changes in life that feel overwhelming

- Being exposed to suicide or the death of a peer under any circumstances

WHAT SHOULD TEACHERS AND OTHER SCHOOL STAFF DO IF THEY KNOW OR SUSPECT A TEEN IS SUICIDAL?

The role of teachers and other school staff in the prevention process is critical but limited. Teachers and staff should follow these steps:

1. Stay alert to changes in student behavior that correspond to the FACTS acrostic.

2. Express your concerns to the student, if you feel comfortable doing so.

3. Immediately notify internal school resources if the situation seems especially worrisome (the student is making threats or you hear about an attempt). These staff members have the training and skills to

    - talk more in depth with the student

    - decide whether or not parents or guardians need to be informed

    - decide if further assessment by a mental health professional is required

WHY SHOULD OUR SCHOOL IMPLEMENT A SUICIDE PREVENTION EDUCATION PROGRAM?

Very few suicides or suicide attempts take place in schools. But many young people who are at risk for suicide exhibit warning signs in school, and the ability to recognize and act on these warning signs could prevent death or injuries and reduce emotional suffering.

As national data clearly demonstrate, these at-risk youths are sitting in classrooms all over the country. Ignoring their presence does not make them go away. This will not help their peers who may realize something is wrong but don't know how to be helpful. And it doesn't provide support or direction to their teachers who also sense there is a problem but are uncertain on whether to intervene.

A suicide prevention education program is a pragmatic, proactive approach that supports the prevention of self-destructive behavior by students. It is grounded in the perspective of the school as a competent community where school officials clearly and consistently convey the vision that all members of the school care deeply about the safety and positive development of each other.

An increasing body of literature suggests that conceptualizing schools as competent and caring communities has a wide range of positive outcomes, which includes more effectively meeting the needs of both teachers and students. Most schools currently apply this concept of community to the prevention of interpersonal violence. "Safe" school mandates clearly outline responses to threats against others. Suicide prevention programs are the logical extensions of "safe" schools and send an important message to the entire student body: *your* life is just as important as the lives of others.

INTRO-2, INTRO-3   For more information on youth suicide, see Frequently Asked Questions about Youth Suicide on the CD-ROM. For an in-depth case study on one state's implementation of *Lifelines*, see Notes from the Field on the CD-ROM.

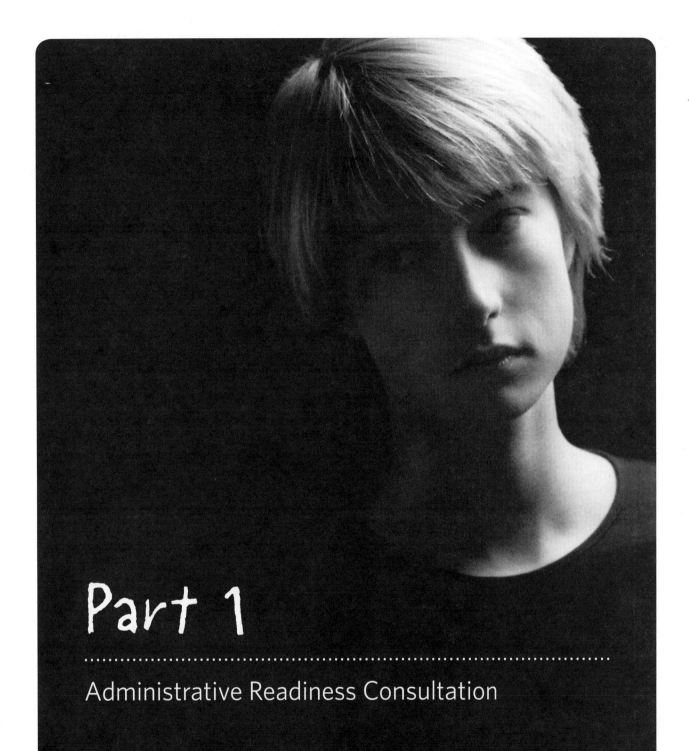

Part 1

Administrative Readiness Consultation

Administrative Readiness Consultation

....

INTRODUCTION

The foundation for any school-based suicide awareness program must begin at the administrative level with the development of school policies and procedures for handling at-risk or suicidal students, and for responding in the event of a suicide. These procedures are designed to help schools quickly mobilize a coordinated support system for students in crisis, and to identify resources within both the school and the local community for responding to suicide emergencies. The emphasis in procedures is on the school's role as a liaison, clearly referring the treatment responsibility to other community resources.

There are two reasons why the establishment of policies and procedures is a critical first step:

1. They represent the school's concrete recognition of the special issues presented by suicidal or at-risk teens and, in some ways, a demonstration of the school's commitment to interventions for these students.

2. They can reassure the faculty that a system exists for referral of students who might be at risk. This responsibility will not remain with teachers who are generally already overburdened with academic responsibilities. A clear definition of a response hierarchy in a suicidal crisis can begin to address faculty concern about assuming yet another responsibility.

The intent of these procedures is to provide a coordinated support system for students in crisis in the most quietly efficient manner possible. Written procedures

21

also serve as a concrete reminder that the obligation to begin possible life-saving intervention takes precedence over the commitment to student confidentiality. This reinforces the school's role as a competent and compassionate community.

Advanced planning to prevent youth suicide and to intervene in a crisis can significantly improve the ability of school personnel to respond quickly, effectively, and with the least disruption to school routines when suicidal behavior becomes an issue. This can be best accomplished by having in place:

- school personnel or resource staff who have been clearly designated as points of contact and have been trained to respond to the student and collaborate with parents and local resources

- liaison procedures with local mental health agencies

- clear guidelines that provide ideal responses to various suicidal situations and that are distributed to all school staff

The response chain of command should be clearly stated, with the identification of appropriate backups. Any requirements for written documentation should be created as standard forms and attached to the policies that are given to faculty and staff. A faculty in-service can provide a forum for discussing the policy, the reasons for its implementation, and examples of how it is to be used.

IS YOUR SCHOOL PREPARED TO MANAGE SUICIDAL BEHAVIOR?

 P1-4

While not an exhaustive list, the questions in the following screening tool will help you develop the necessary school protocols to address suicide prevention, intervention, and postvention. (A printable copy of the readiness survey can be found on the CD-ROM.) After answering the questions, compare the guidelines on pages 33–41 with your school's established policies and procedures. Remember, these are guidelines and they can be modified to fit your school's needs. The overall goal is to provide as smooth, efficient, and maximally supportive response to these situations as is possible.

Readiness Survey

Administrative Questions

A. Prevention refers to proactive activities designed to prepare a school for effective, timely responses to students who may be at risk for suicide.

1. Does your school have an up-to-date crisis response plan?

○ YES ○ NO ○ NEED TO CONSIDER

COMMENTS:

2. Does the crisis response plan have solid administrative support?

○ YES ○ NO ○ NEED TO CONSIDER

COMMENTS:

3a. Does the crisis response plan have written protocols on how to manage suicidal (student and/or staff) behavior?

○ YES ○ NO ○ NEED TO CONSIDER

COMMENTS:

3b. Does the crisis response plan have written protocols on how to manage a suicidal (student and/or staff) attempt on campus?

○ YES ○ NO ○ NEED TO CONSIDER

COMMENTS:

3c. Does the crisis response plan have written protocols on how to manage a suicidal (student and/or staff) attempt off campus?

○ YES ○ NO ○ NEED TO CONSIDER

COMMENTS:

4a. Have crisis team members been identified?

○ YES ○ NO ○ NEED TO CONSIDER

COMMENTS:

4b. Are individuals from both the school and the community involved in the crisis team?

○ YES   ○ NO   ○ NEED TO CONSIDER

COMMENTS:

5. Are crisis team members provided with training?

○ YES   ○ NO   ○ NEED TO CONSIDER

COMMENTS:

6. Are substitute crisis team members identified in case regular members are not available due to absence, conference attendance, vacation, and so forth?

○ YES   ○ NO   ○ NEED TO CONSIDER

COMMENTS:

7. Would the crisis team be able to support multiple schools in the event of a murder/suicide situation? (For example, a parent murders siblings attending several different schools and then takes his or her own life.)

○ YES   ○ NO   ○ NEED TO CONSIDER

COMMENTS:

8. Do crisis team members have copies of school floor plans for their use and/or to provide to local law enforcement, if needed?

○ YES   ○ NO   ○ NEED TO CONSIDER

COMMENTS:

9. Does the crisis team meet and practice simulations on a regular basis?

○ YES   ○ NO   ○ NEED TO CONSIDER

COMMENTS:

10. Are copies of the school crisis plan readily accessible to all school personnel?

○ YES   ○ NO   ○ NEED TO CONSIDER

COMMENTS:

11a. Is there an established method for distributing protocols that includes who should receive them?

○ YES   ○ NO   ○ NEED TO CONSIDER

COMMENTS:

11b. Is there a plan for providing new staff with protocols?

○ YES   ○ NO   ○ NEED TO CONSIDER

COMMENTS:

12. Has school administration provided clear direction about legal rights and obligations of administrators, faculty, and staff in assisting with a suicidal student?

○ YES   ○ NO   ○ NEED TO CONSIDER

COMMENTS:

13. Is someone designated to track the number of suicides, suicide attempts, and/or referrals for suicidal behavior?

○ YES   ○ NO   ○ NEED TO CONSIDER

COMMENTS:

14. Has a policy for maintaining confidentiality of sensitive student information been created and disseminated to all school personnel?

○ YES   ○ NO   ○ NEED TO CONSIDER

COMMENTS:

15a. Does the school have a formal memorandum of agreement (MOA) with the local crisis service provider(s) outlining the services to be provided to the school system such as risk assessments, crisis management, and/or debriefing school staff in the aftermath of a crisis?

○ YES   ○ NO   ○ NEED TO CONSIDER

COMMENTS:

15b. Does the MOA include debriefing parents and community members in the event of a suicide?

○ YES   ○ NO   ○ NEED TO CONSIDER

COMMENTS:

16. Does the MOA include guidelines for how the school receives feedback on the outcomes of the referrals that are made?

○ YES   ○ NO   ○ NEED TO CONSIDER

COMMENTS:

17. Have school administrators, faculty, and staff received education and training in suicide prevention?

○ YES   ○ NO   ○ NEED TO CONSIDER

COMMENTS:

18a. Has an effective student suicide prevention education program been incorporated into the comprehensive health education program?

○ YES   ○ NO   ○ NEED TO CONSIDER

COMMENTS:

18b. Does the program focus on building help-seeking skills? (Note: The student component should only be introduced after protocols have been established, MOAs are in place, staff education has occurred, and key staff identified as those who can help with suicidal behavior.)

○ YES   ○ NO   ○ NEED TO CONSIDER

COMMENTS:

19. Has a discussion with law enforcement occurred so that you know what to expect from the local law enforcement agency in the event of a crisis in school buildings or on school grounds?

○ YES   ○ NO   ○ NEED TO CONSIDER

COMMENTS:

20. Has the traffic pattern to and from the school been reviewed with emergency response personnel?

○ YES   ○ NO   ○ NEED TO CONSIDER

COMMENTS:

B. Intervention refers to an outline of specific actions to be implemented in response to suicidal behavior.

21. Do school procedures/protocols identify key people within each building as contacts to help when suicidal behavior occurs?

○ YES   ○ NO   ○ NEED TO CONSIDER

COMMENTS:

22. Do school procedures designate someone to contact the parents/guardians when suicide risk is suspected?

○ YES   ○ NO   ○ NEED TO CONSIDER

COMMENTS:

23. Does the school have procedures for when the parents/guardians are unreachable?

○ YES   ○ NO   ○ NEED TO CONSIDER

COMMENTS:

24. Does the school have procedures for when parents/guardians refuse to get help for their child?

○ YES   ○ NO   ○ NEED TO CONSIDER

COMMENTS:

25. Does the school provide information to parents/guardians about the importance of removing lethal means?

○ YES   ○ NO   ○ NEED TO CONSIDER

COMMENTS:

26a. Does the school have a system to alert staff of an emergency while school is in session?
○ YES　○ NO　○ NEED TO CONSIDER
COMMENTS:

26b. Have volunteers and substitutes been informed about the system?
○ YES　○ NO　○ NEED TO CONSIDER
COMMENTS:

27. Are there protocols concerning how to help students re-enter school after an absence or hospitalization for mental illness including suicidal behavior?
○ YES　○ NO　○ NEED TO CONSIDER
COMMENTS:

28. Are there systems/teams in place to address the needs of students who are exhibiting high-risk behaviors such as substance abuse, depression, or self-injury?
○ YES　○ NO　○ NEED TO CONSIDER
COMMENTS:

C. Postvention refers to a sequence of planned support and interventions carried out in the aftermath of a suicide with the intention of preventing suicide contagion.

29a. Do the protocols include a section about working with the media?
○ YES　○ NO　○ NEED TO CONSIDER
COMMENTS:

29b. Has a spokesperson been designated?
○ YES　○ NO　○ NEED TO CONSIDER
COMMENTS:

29c. Is there a backup for that person?
○ YES　○ NO　○ NEED TO CONSIDER
COMMENTS:

30a. In the event of a suicide, are there established protocols for identifying close friends/ other vulnerable students and plans to support them?

○ YES   ○ NO   ○ NEED TO CONSIDER

COMMENTS:

30b. Does this protocol include students at other buildings?

○ YES   ○ NO   ○ NEED TO CONSIDER

COMMENTS:

30c. Does this protocol include staff that might be affected due to either their relationship with the youth or their own experience with suicide in their families?

○ YES   ○ NO   ○ NEED TO CONSIDER

COMMENTS:

31. Do the protocols consider the fact that, following a suicide, whole-school and/or permanent memorials are *not* recommended?

○ YES   ○ NO   ○ NEED TO CONSIDER

COMMENTS:

Staff-related Questions

1. Have *all* staff members received training about suicide prevention?

○ YES   ○ NO   ○ NEED TO CONSIDER

COMMENTS:

2. Have *all* staff members been provided with the school protocols?

○ YES   ○ NO   ○ NEED TO CONSIDER

COMMENTS:

3a. Have trained resource staff members been identified as contacts for when a staff member or student wants to ask about suicidal behavior?
○ YES   ○ NO   ○ NEED TO CONSIDER
COMMENTS:

3b. Has everyone in the building been informed of who the resource staff members are?
○ YES   ○ NO   ○ NEED TO CONSIDER
COMMENTS:

4. Do staff members know what to do in the event that they come upon or hear about a suicide incident?
○ YES   ○ NO   ○ NEED TO CONSIDER
COMMENTS:

5. Have the confidentiality guidelines been provided and discussed with *all* staff members?
○ YES   ○ NO   ○ NEED TO CONSIDER
COMMENTS:

6. Do school protocols guide staff members on what to look for and what to do if they find student work/messages (such as artwork, doodling, homework, term papers, journal entries, or notes) that focus on death or suicide?
○ YES   ○ NO   ○ NEED TO CONSIDER
COMMENTS:

7. Will teachers receive feedback on students whom they refer for an evaluation of suicidal risk?
○ YES   ○ NO   ○ NEED TO CONSIDER
COMMENTS:

8. Do staff members understand that it is not their responsibility to assess the seriousness of a situation but that suicidal behavior must be taken seriously and reported using the school protocols?

   ○ YES   ○ NO   ○ NEED TO CONSIDER

   COMMENTS:

9. Do the protocols inform staff members about what to do if there is any reason to suspect a weapon is present/readily available?

   ○ YES   ○ NO   ○ NEED TO CONSIDER

   COMMENTS:

10. Are procedures in place to brief and debrief staff members in the event of a crisis?

    ○ YES   ○ NO   ○ NEED TO CONSIDER

    COMMENTS:

Parent-related Questions

1. Are opportunities provided for parents/guardians to learn about suicide prevention?

   ○ YES   ○ NO   ○ NEED TO CONSIDER

   COMMENTS:

2. Are there efforts to actively communicate with parents/guardians about risk factors, warning signs, and the importance of restricting access to lethal means?

   ○ YES   ○ NO   ○ NEED TO CONSIDER

   COMMENTS:

3. Have parents/guardians been told what the school is doing to prevent and address the issue of suicide, what will be done if their son or daughter is thought to be at risk of suicide, and what will be expected of them?

   ○ YES   ○ NO   ○ NEED TO CONSIDER

   COMMENTS:

4. Are parents/guardians provided with a current list of community resources and agencies to contact if they are concerned that their son or daughter is suicidal?

○ YES   ○ NO   ○ NEED TO CONSIDER

COMMENTS:

Student-related Questions

1a. Are students educated about suicide and how to help a troubled friend?

○ YES   ○ NO   ○ NEED TO CONSIDER

COMMENTS:

1b. Does the education include practicing an intervention?

○ YES   ○ NO   ○ NEED TO CONSIDER

COMMENTS:

2. Do students know whom to go to in the school if they are worried about a suicidal friend?

○ YES   ○ NO   ○ NEED TO CONSIDER

COMMENTS:

3. Are behavioral health services readily available to youth?

○ YES   ○ NO   ○ NEED TO CONSIDER

COMMENTS:

POLICY AND PROCEDURES GUIDELINES

The following suicide prevention, intervention, and postvention guidelines are designed for schools to use within existing protocols to assist at-risk students and intervene appropriately in suicide-related crises. They are drawn from actual school policies that were reviewed by the Maine Youth Suicide Prevention Program.[1] They recognize and build on the skills and resources inherent in school administrative units. School boards and school personnel may choose to implement additional supportive measures to fit the needs of an individual school community. The purpose of these guidelines is to assist school administrators in their planning. The guidelines do not constitute legal advice, nor are they intended to do so.

Guidelines for Responding to the At-risk Student

Low or Unclear Risk

Definition: Low or unclear risk of suicide is raised when any peer, teacher, or other school employee identifies a student as potentially suicidal because he or she has directly or indirectly expressed suicidal thoughts (ideation) or demonstrated other clues or warning signs.

1. Take the threat of self-harm seriously.

2. Take immediate action. Contact the building administrator or designated staff person to inform him or her of the situation.

3. The designated staff person trained in suicide prevention meets with the student and does a basic screening that includes specific questions to determine the existence of a suicide plan.

4. Parents/guardians must always be notified when there appears to be any risk of self-harm, unless it is apparent that such notification will worsen the situation (see #5 below). The individual who notifies the parent should be an administrator or other person who has the experience/expertise and/or a special relationship with the student and parents. Resource information should be provided if needed. The same person should follow up with the parents within a few days to determine what has been done.

5. If those school personnel working with a student feel that child protective service interventions are indicated, such contact must be initiated (per district policy).

6. If necessary, the prearranged crisis service agency should be contacted to access the appropriate crisis intervention agency. This call should result in obtaining consultation with a professional who has the skills, authority, and responsibility to formally assess the student for suicidality and the necessary level of care.

 P1-1

7. Print out and complete the Report of Suicide Risk form on the CD-ROM.

Medium- to High-Risk Situations

Definition: Medium to high risk exists when a staff person observes *verbal or non-verbal interpersonal action stopping short of a directly self-harmful act* that communicates or suggests that the student wishes to die or may attempt suicide. The intent of the student making the threat cannot be determined until a thorough assessment is completed.

1. All staff members understand that they must *always* take suicidal behavior seriously.

2. The staff person "on the scene" takes immediate action to inform the building administrator. The administrator will locate the trained staff person designated to respond to such situations. Alternates will be identified in the event of unavailability of staff due to conference attendance, illness, vacation, and so forth.

3. The staff person on the scene talks with the student, staying calm and listening attentively. It is crucial to keep the student under continuous adult supervision until the designated trained staff person arrives.

4. The trained staff member conducts a basic suicide risk assessment with the student to determine the lethality of the threat. This includes
   a. determining if the student has a plan
   b. asking if the student has lethal means on his or her person or accessible elsewhere
   c. consulting with a crisis service provider if necessary to obtain an assessment of the student's mental state and a recommendation for treatment

5. If the student is in possession of lethal means, secure the area and prevent other students from accessing this area. Lethal means must be removed

without putting anyone in danger. It is best to call a trained law enforcement officer to remove lethal means. Law enforcement officers have special training to de-escalate a situation that can very quickly become dangerous (such as possession of a gun or knife).

6. The administrator (or designated staff person) contacts the parents or guardians to

    a. notify them of the situation and request that they come to school

    b. provide them with a full report on arrival at school

    c. inform them that the student cannot return to school until he or she has been appropriately assessed and medical clearance has been obtained. The staff person provides referral resources for such assessment, including contact information. Parents or guardians are expected to obtain the assessment in a timely manner in order to address the medical needs of the student. Print out and complete the Referral Information for Parents form on the CD-ROM.

    P1-2

7. If those school personnel working with a student feel that intervention from state child protective services is indicated, such contact must be initiated (per district policy), especially if the student's safety is at risk.

8. School staff are expected to keep the student under continuous adult supervision until the above steps are completed and the student is released to his or her parents/guardians.

9. A designated resource staff member will contact the appropriate administrator (principal/vice-principal) and explain the intervention.

10. The principal or principal's designee will notify the superintendent of schools and/or director of special services.

11. In the event that the situation requires transportation to a hospital emergency department, crisis services and/or law enforcement should be contacted to assess the situation and expedite the transition to the hospital.

12. Prior to re-entry/re-admission to school the parents/guardians are responsible for obtaining an appropriate assessment. The assessment must be conducted by a licensed mental health practitioner or psychiatric emergency services center.

13. Prior to re-admission to school, a re-entry conference must be scheduled in order to discuss appropriate supports necessary for transition back to school.

14. Written documentation must be provided to the school stating that the assessment has been conducted. This documentation must clearly indicate that the student has been medically cleared (is safe) to return to school.

P1-1

15. Print out and complete the Report of Suicide Risk form on the CD-ROM.

16. All staff members who assisted with the intervention are debriefed.

Guidelines for Responding to a Suicide Attempt

Attempt On School Premises

Procedures for Assisting the Suicidal Student

1. Keep the student physically safe and under close supervision.

2. The school nurse will secure immediate medical treatment, using either first aid techniques or calling 9-1-1.

3. One or more staff members should be designated to stay with and support the student in crisis while help is being sought.

4. Notify the school administrator or designated staff person who will immediately communicate with designated individuals such as crisis or student assistance team members, the school nurse, social worker or counselor, emergency and medical professionals, community crisis service providers, law enforcement, and the superintendent of schools.

5. Notify the parents/guardians of what has occurred and arrange to meet them wherever appropriate.

6. Consult with crisis service agency staff as necessary to assess the student's mental state and to obtain a recommendation for needed treatment.

7. A representative from the school should accompany the student to the hospital if medical treatment is necessary prior to the parents' or guardians' arrival at school.

8. If the student does not require emergency treatment or hospitalization and the immediate crisis is under control, release the student to the parents/guardians with arrangements for needed medical treatment and/or mental health counseling.

9. In the event that the situation requires transportation to a hospital emergency department, crisis services, emergency medical services, and/or law enforcement should be contacted to assess the situation and expedite the transition to the hospital.

10. Inform parents/guardians that the student cannot return to school until the student has been appropriately assessed and medical clearance has been obtained.

11. Establish a plan for periodic contact with the student while away from school.

12. Make arrangements, if necessary, for class assignments to be completed at home.

13. Other school policies that apply to a student's extended absence should be followed. Print out and read through Issues and Options Surrounding a Student's Return to School Following a Suicide-related Absence on the CD-ROM. **P1-3**

14. Print out and complete the Report of Suicide Risk form on the CD-ROM. **P1-1**

15. Debrief all staff members involved in the intervention.

Procedures for Assisting Other Students during a Crisis

1. During the crisis, clear the area of other students immediately. Remove students who witnessed the event to a private area where a crisis team member can debrief them. It is best to keep the general student body in current classrooms and provide a supportive presence until the emergency situation is under control.

2. Alert classroom teachers to the situation through text messages or other previously established methods of communication.

3. Provide teachers with a short scripted message to communicate to students. Unless the entire student body witnessed the event, *do not* provide information about either the student or situation. Partial information

can contribute to chaos. (Use language such as "Our school is having a crisis response drill. We will remain in the classroom until we get further instructions.")

4. The superintendent or designated staff person alerts principals at schools attended by siblings, who in turn will notify counselors, nurses, and others in a position to help siblings and other students who might be affected.

5. A faculty meeting may be called by the principal or principal's designee at the end of the day to inform teachers of the event, offer them an opportunity to address their feelings and concerns, and plan appropriate procedures for subsequent school days. Students who may be affected by a suicide attempt should be identified by appropriate staff members by informing the student's guidance counselor. A follow-up plan should be developed to help support any identified situations where services could be provided via the guidance department or crisis response team.

Attempt Off School Premises

1. If the suicide attempt is made at home and the parents/guardians share this information with the school, a member of the crisis intervention team will contact the family immediately and offer assistance in whatever way is deemed necessary. The parents or guardians will be informed of the school's policy regarding the need to obtain medical/psychiatric "clearance" prior to re-entry to school.

2. If students are aware of the attempt, follow established procedures for outreach to vulnerable students.

Guidelines for When a Student Returns to School Following a Suicide Attempt

1. Prior to the student's return, a meeting between the student, the student's parents/guardians, and a designated school staff member such as the school nurse, social worker, administrator, or other designated staff person should be scheduled to discuss possible arrangements for support services and to create an individualized re-entry plan.

2. The designated school staff member should

   a. review and file written documents as part of the student's confidential health record

b. serve as case manager for the student. They should understand what precipitated the suicide attempt and be alert to what might precipitate another attempt. They should also be familiar with practical aspects of the case, such as medications and full versus partial study load recommendations.

c. help the student through re-admission procedures, monitor the re-entry, and serve as a contact for other staff members who need to be alert to re-occurring warning signs

d. serve as a link with the parents/guardians, and, with the written permission of the parents/guardians, serve as the school liaison with any external medical or mental health service providers supporting the student

3. Classroom teachers *do* need to know whether the student is on a full or partial study load and should be updated on the student's progress in general. They *do not* need clinical information or a detailed history.

4. Discussion of the case among personnel directly involved in supporting the student should be conducted in private settings and be specifically related to the student's treatment and support needs. Discussion of the student among other staff should be strictly on a need-to-know basis, that is, information directly related to what staff have to know in order to work with the student.

Guidelines for Responding to a Suicide Completion

1. If news of a death by suicide is received, the principal or the principal's designee will verify the information with the police and notify the superintendent of schools immediately.

2. If news is received during the school day, siblings or other family members of the deceased should be escorted to the principal's office and sent home with responsible adult supervision.

3. All contacts with the news media should be referred to the superintendent of schools who will be responsible for ensuring that information is handled in such a manner as to discourage sensationalism in the coverage of the tragedy.

4. In an effort to responsibly deal with the emotional reactions within the

school community and to decrease the potential for a contagious effect, the following procedures should be initiated:

a. If news of the suicide is received during the school day, faculty should be alerted by the pre-established communication strategy and provided with basic information about the event. Crisis team members should be involved in this notification to faculty members and staff who are known to have had a close relationship or contact with the deceased student.

b. The crisis team should begin immediate identification of high-risk students. Team members should reach out to these students and their parents prior to dismissal to ensure they will receive appropriate parental and mental health support as the crisis unfolds.

c. The principal will call an emergency faculty meeting at the conclusion of the day in order to disclose all relevant facts pertaining to the tragic news and to outline procedures to be followed in the subsequent days and weeks.

d. If news of the suicide is received over the weekend or during vacation, an emergency faculty meeting should be called before the students arrive on the first school day. Staff contact should be made using the school's standard staff contact system.

e. All information will be distributed using a prepared statement. The principal or the principal's designee may enlist the assistance of the administration, guidance counselors, child study team, and nurses in order to convey the information to the student population. Information presented to the students must be factual, and students and staff should not speculate over unconfirmed reports or rumors.

5. Community resources (such as members of the clergy and other appropriate resource individuals) will be mobilized to assist school personnel in counseling students, family members, and any other concerned community members. The use of external mental health consultants can serve to legitimize the school's postvention processes and can maintain a neutral and objective stance in an emotionally charged situation. Ideally, these resources should also be associated with the local mental health service, which can be expected to provide follow-up services to any students requiring them. In this way, these consultants can help negotiate any bureaucratic barriers that might otherwise interfere with prompt and responsive assistance.

6. The superintendent, principal, or principal's designee will prepare a written statement for the purpose of assisting all teachers in maintaining consis-

tency in reporting the facts surrounding the suicide to students. *Under no circumstances should students be informed of the suicide in a large assembly.* If possible, students should be informed about the facts in small groups rather than through the public address system.

7. Experience has indicated that many students will need an opportunity to share their feelings about the deceased. These sessions should be conducted by child study team guidance personnel who have been trained in appropriate procedures. The school principal should have already prepared an outline of areas where students may receive counseling during the postvention. *Students should be in supervised areas at all times.*

8. Students should be allowed to leave class for purposes of grief management and support. While some students will take advantage of this permission, this should not become a paramount concern in determining whether or not a student should be permitted to leave class. Appropriate staff members should identify students who may be affected by the death of a student and subsequently inform the student's guidance counselor. This person will facilitate a referral to either a support group or crisis team member for individual support and assessment. A follow-up plan will be developed to help support any students identified for services provided via the guidance department.

9. To the extent possible, efforts should be made to ensure that the regular school routine is followed. However, it is advisable that stressful activities, such as major examinations, be rescheduled for later dates. *Activities to be avoided include special memorial services, flying the flag at half-mast, permanent memorials, or anything else that might "glamorize" the suicide.*

10. The school will consider the utilization of consultants and community resources in order to provide additional support to students, parents, and staff members.

The procedures outlined above are, of course, subject to variation in certain circumstances. The following issues, however, need to be addressed consistently:

- When a potential suicide risk is present, the parents or guardians are to be contacted and advised of the steps that need to be taken.

- When confronted with an actual situation in which life-threatening behaviors or ideation is present, immediate mobilization of all appropriate resources is paramount.

RATIONALE FOR TEACHING STUDENTS SUICIDE PREVENTIVE INTERVENTION STEPS

Adults are usually the last to know about a suicidal youth, so students must be taught how to respond to peers who may be exhibiting suicidal behaviors.

A few facts:

- Most suicidal youths share their concerns with their peers far more often than with adults.

- Disturbed youth (e.g., depressed, substance abusers) prefer peer supports to adults more than their nondisturbed peers.

- Some adolescents, particularly some males, do not respond to troubled peers in empathic or helpful ways.

- As few as 25 percent of peer confidants tell an adult about a troubled or suicidal peer.

- School personnel are consistently among the *last* choices of adolescents for discussing personal concerns.

- Consistent reasons cited by students for reluctance to confide in adults in their schools include:

  - Confidentiality is not respected.

  - Adults do not have the time to listen due to school schedules and other demands.

  - School schedules and other organizational characteristics prevent students from getting to know adults well enough to feel comfortable confiding in them.

The perceived inaccessibility and reluctance of adolescents to seek out helpful adults contributes to destructive outcomes associated with a variety of adolescent risk behaviors.

- Contrary to students' perceptions, research has shown that contact with helpful adults may be considered a *protective factor* for troubled youth.

- There is also evidence that youths themselves benefit from helping others. Participation in helping interactions can shape prosocial behaviors and reduce problematic behavior. In addition, youths practice social competencies that can carry over into other challenging situations.

LIFELINES IMPLEMENTATION PROCEDURE

Schools must be prepared to respond to the referrals of at-risk teens that suicide response programs generate. Thus the implementation of *Lifelines* begins with a review of school policies and procedures by administrators and/or committees designated to develop such procedures. Some schools already have procedures in place, and this initial meeting will simply consist of a review and identification of contact persons in the local human services system.

After the administrative readiness consultation (part 1), steps are taken as necessary to formalize links between the school system and prevention and crisis intervention services through memorandums of agreement. Meanwhile, suicide prevention education is provided to faculty, other school staff, and parents (parts 2 and 3). There can be a variety of formats and content in these presentations, as long as the emphasis is on information that has practical implications for educators and parents. Presentations that contain clinical or mental health jargon or abstract statistics are (appropriately) not well received.

The student sessions are the core of the *Lifelines* program (part 4). This material is developmentally appropriate for eighth through twelfth grades. However, it is best suited for eighth, ninth, or tenth grade. Students in eleventh and twelfth grades are beginning to deal with transitions to work or college, and these issues would need to be addressed (such as how to find resources on a college campus). Below eighth grade, topics such as death or help-seeking behavior would have to be approached differently.

In keeping with the goal of the entire program, the focus of the classroom curriculum is practical and action oriented. Given the critical role of peers in suicidal situations, the lessons are directed toward teaching youth how to recognize and reach out to troubled peers.

Most adolescents are struggling with issues of autonomy and separation from adult support, and, in this process, place a good deal of importance on loyalty to peers. This developmental issue presents a dilemma in that students must be encouraged to seek adult help for a suicidal peer. The curriculum directly addresses the dilemma, and teachers are encouraged to extend the discussion beyond the specific exercises in the sessions.

Program Evaluation

Evaluations of the *Lifelines* program to date have yielded very positive results. Compared to nonparticipating controls,

- educators have demonstrated significant gains in knowledge of suicide warning signs and community resources, and positive attitudes toward intervening with and referring at-risk youth

- students have more "tell an adult" responses on questionnaires and in response to vignettes

PROJECT OVERVIEW OF *LIFELINES*

Overall Program Goal

The goal of *Lifelines* is to increase the likelihood that school administrators, faculty, staff, and students who come into contact with at-risk youth will more readily identify them, provide an appropriate initial response, know how to obtain help, and consistently take such action.

Program Components	Objectives
Part 1: **Administrative Readiness Consultation**	• All faculty and staff will know school procedure for responding to suicidal situations. • School officials (administrators and other school personnel designated to respond to suicidal situations) will know community providers and referral procedures.
Part 2: **Training for School Faculty and Staff**	• All faculty and staff will know relevant suicide facts, indicators of at-risk students, and response guidelines, including referral procedures.
Part 3: **Parent Workshop**	• Parents will know how to identify at-risk teens, be familiar with resources, and support the school program.
Part 4: **Student Curriculum**	• Students will demonstrate positive attitudes about intervention and help-seeking for themselves and others. • Students will know relevant facts about suicide, including warning signs. • Students will know how to respond to troubled peers. • Students will know resources for help, be able to name one helpful adult, and know how resources will respond.

FEATURES OF *LIFELINES* STUDENT SESSIONS

A number of features have been incorporated into the *Lifelines* student sessions to make them easily adaptable to the realities of school systems.

Class Schedules

The sessions are organized into four 45-minute lesson plans that can be incorporated into existing health classes. They can be easily adapted to two 90-minute sessions. No time outside of class is required for students or teachers, and no expansion of already overburdened school curricula is necessary. It should be noted that there is a high correlation between adolescent suicide and other topics that are often part of health classes such as substance abuse, mental health issues, and teen pregnancy.

Educational Focus

The lesson plans are based on sound educational principles of interactive teaching (see pages 48–51). They are devoid of mental health jargon. The sessions focus on issues that students are currently dealing with such as keeping confidences. Activities and the use of videos promote participatory learning. Each session is limited to three or four basic points, which is the most that students (teens and adults alike) will likely retain in a 45-minute period.

Teacher Provided

The sessions are designed for presentation by regular classroom teachers rather than external consultants. This is cost-effective as well as consistent with the goal of enhancing school-based student supports. Research indicates that students are more likely to talk about their concerns with an adult who has demonstrated interest and expertise in that area. Therefore, when classroom teachers cover material on suicide, students may see them as concerned, responsive adults who are available during school hours.

Students have also reported that they perceive staff and faculty who take the time to interact with them outside of their office or classroom as helpful. Thus, presenting the curriculum can enhance the credibility of a teacher, but additional interaction with students may be necessary to increase the likelihood that students will see the teacher as a resource.

RELATED NATIONAL ACADEMIC STANDARDS[2]

Students in grades six through eight will

- Analyze the relationship between healthy behaviors and personal health.
- Describe the interrelationships of emotional, intellectual, physical, and social health in adolescence.
- Describe ways to reduce or prevent injuries and other adolescent health problems.
- Examine the likelihood of injury or illness if engaging in unhealthy behaviors.
- Examine the potential seriousness of injury or illness if engaging in unhealthy behaviors.
- Describe how peers influence healthy and unhealthy behaviors.
- Analyze how the school and community can affect personal health practices and behaviors.
- Determine the accessibility of products that enhance health.
- Describe situations that may require professional health services.
- Locate valid and reliable health products and services.
- Apply effective verbal and nonverbal communication skills to enhance health.
- Demonstrate refusal or negotiation skills that avoid or reduce health risks.
- Demonstrate effective conflict management or resolution strategies.
- Demonstrate how to ask for assistance to enhance the health of self or others.
- Identify circumstances that can help or hinder healthy decision making.
- Determine when health-related situations require the application of a thoughtful decision-making process.
- Distinguish when individual or collaborative decision making is appropriate.
- Distinguish between healthy and unhealthy alternatives to health-related issues or problems.
- Predict the potential short-term impact of each alternative on self or others.
- Analyze the outcomes of a health-related decision.
- Demonstrate healthy practices and behaviors that will maintain or improve the health of self and others.

- Demonstrate behaviors that avoid or reduce health risks to self and others.

- State a health-enhancing position on a topic and support it with accurate information.

- Demonstrate how to influence and support others to make positive health choices.

- Work cooperatively to advocate for healthy individuals, families, and schools.

Students in grades nine through twelve will

- Predict how healthy behaviors can affect health status.

- Describe the interrelationships of emotional, intellectual, physical, and social health.

- Propose ways to reduce or prevent injuries and health problems.

- Analyze the relationship between access to health care and health status.

- Analyze personal susceptibility to injury, illness, or death if engaging in unhealthy behaviors.

- Analyze the potential severity of injury or illness if engaging in unhealthy behaviors.

- Analyze how peers influence healthy and unhealthy behaviors.

- Evaluate how the school and community can affect personal health practices and behaviors.

- Evaluate the validity of health information, products, and services.

- Determine the accessibility of products and services that enhance health.

- Determine when professional health services may be required.

- Access valid and reliable health products and services.

- Use skills for communicating effectively with family, peers, and others to enhance health.

- Demonstrate refusal, negotiation, and collaboration skills to enhance health and avoid or reduce health risks.

- Demonstrate strategies to prevent, manage, or resolve interpersonal conflicts without harming self or others.

- Demonstrate how to ask for and offer assistance to enhance the health of self or others.

- Examine barriers that can hinder healthy decision making.

- Determine the value of applying a thoughtful decision-making process in health-related situations.

- Justify when individual or collaborative decision making is appropriate.

- Generate alternatives to health-related issues or problems.

- Predict the potential short-term and long-term impact of each alternative on self and others.

- Defend the healthy choice when making decisions.

- Evaluate the effectiveness of health-related decisions.

- Demonstrate a variety of healthy practices and behaviors that will maintain or improve the health of self and others.

- Demonstrate a variety of behaviors that avoid or reduce health risks to self and others.

- Demonstrate how to influence and support others to make positive health choices.

- Work cooperatively as an advocate for improving personal, family, and community health.

SOCIAL DEVELOPMENT STRATEGY AND INTERACTIVE TEACHING

The Social Development Strategy was developed by Dr. David Hawkins and Dr. Richard Catalano (University of Washington in Seattle) to reduce the risk of children using drugs.[3] It grew out of forty-plus years of Social Learning Theory and Social Control Theory on how to maintain or extinguish patterns of behavior and of learning. The strategy works very well when teaching prevention programs. It is all about behavior change and adapts well to suicide prevention efforts.

According to the Social Development Strategy, in order to encourage individuals to believe in and support a "desired behavior," we have to (1) provide meaningful opportunities to participate in or strive for the desired behavior; (2) teach the skills necessary to perform the desired behavior; and (3) give consistent recognition for performing as expected, and provide constructive feedback when behavior is inappropriate. These three things—opportunities, skills, and recognition—are the qualities that develop and maintain strong bonds to the ideas (positive norms) and the people (positive influences) that will ultimately lead to the desired behavior.

Given that suicidal behavior threatens the well-being of the youth at risk *and* his or her friends and family, the objective of the *Lifelines* curriculum is to "sell" the concept that suicide is preventable and that turning to a trusted adult for help is an appropriate youth-driven intervention.

How to Teach This Kind of Behavior Change

It is known that many youths are reluctant to turn to adults for help with suicidal behavior. They can easily tell us all the reasons why they prefer not to tell adults. Given where they are developmentally (detaching from family and attaching to peers), we would expect them to resist the idea of telling adults. It is important to "hear" them, acknowledge their reluctance to "tell," and get them to "buy in" to the idea of turning to a trusted adult for help with suicidal behavior. Interactive teaching is one suggested model for accomplishing this objective.

"Interactive teaching" means that the teacher is very clear about the objective and teaches to that objective throughout the teaching process, never losing sight of the objective and staying in touch with the whole class as they proceed. It maximizes the number of students who hear the message and minimizes the number who get lost. The qualities of interactive teaching are defined below, along with the aspects of *Lifelines* that meet these guidelines. One of the *Lifelines* pilot project schools in Maine used an interactive teaching process, tracking every step of the way. Interestingly enough, that is the school where the intervention is portrayed in the *One Life Saved* video (included on the *Lifelines* DVD).

Steps to Interactive Teaching

1. Mental Set / "buy-in" (cognitive readiness)
2. Input / "telling"
3. Modeling / "showing"
4. Check for Understanding / "asking"
5. Monitor and Adjust / remind, re-model, reinforce
6. Guided Practice / "supervised spontaneity"
7. Gain a Commitment / "confirm"

1. Mental Set

This is about engaging the learners to decide that they want to learn what you want to teach. It is done through tapping their emotions, checking in at a cognitive level, and getting them to acknowledge that what you have to teach has some merit.

Lifelines session 1 (see pages 89–100) creates the mental set in the introduction by establishing that 70 to 80 percent of the students have some connection to someone who has died by suicide. The What Would You Do? exercise in session 1 elicits the students' feelings and actions—and the connection between the two—and provides the opportunity to recognize exactly where they are.

2. Input

This is the "telling" part of teaching to your objective. It can be lecture, storytelling, videos, charts, transparencies—methods that appeal to all kinds of learning styles. This is when skills are named.

The true or false quiz in session 1 initiates the "input" of information, shares more of the facts of suicide, and dispels some of the myths.

The video *A Teen's Guide to Suicide Prevention* shown in session 2 (see pages 101–107) teaches the warning signs and clues, what to do, and what not to do if a friend is suicidal. Addressing the warning signs using the acrostic FACTS provides an opportunity for more input.

The video *One Life Saved* shown in session 3 (see pages 109–117) provides opportunity for the students to "tell" warning signs they noticed as well as outline the intervention steps. Identifying the qualities of helpful people is also an important part of the input.

3. Modeling

This is the "showing" part of teaching to your objective. It reinforces the desired behaviors. It shows people what *can* be done and brings students along to believe that it is a good idea. They are moving from seeing it to doing it ("it" being whatever the skill is that you are trying to teach).

Sessions 2 and 3 begin the modeling process. The videos included in the program (*A Teen's Guide to Suicide Prevention* and *One Life Saved*) model the desired behavior. They show youths asking for help for themselves or their peers. Many videos may relate to the topic of suicide and/or depression, but for the purpose of this class, we must focus on those that demonstrate the behavior we want.

In session 4 (see pages 119–123), students role-play situations in which there is resistance to being helped. Discussion questions provide more modeling experiences. The youth participating in the role-plays perform a "scripted" practice of the objective of the lessons. These individuals have a head start on internalizing what it feels like to find oneself in a position of having to decide what to do.

4. Check for Understanding

This is the "asking" part. It is important to ask questions in a way that lets the majority respond: "How many people know the three basic steps to a suicide intervention?" versus "Dre, what are the three steps to a suicide intervention?" All *Lifelines* sessions provide this opportunity through constant conversation and questions. The role-plays in session 4 check for understanding via student-moderated questions.

5. Monitor and Adjust

Remind, re-input, re-model, and reinforce as necessary. Each lesson in the *Lifelines* curriculum builds on the previous lesson—so it is easy to reinforce the primary objective.

6. Guided Practice (with feedback)

Behavior change is more likely when students (no matter what age) *do* what you want them to do, rather than simply *think* about doing what you want. Practice must be under supervision with safety built in. The main objective is that students leave the classroom situation and *use* the skills, and they are much more likely to use the skills if they participate in some kind of practice—even if they complain that the "practice" is unreal.

Session 4 in *Lifelines* provides a guided practice in the form of scripted role-plays. The discussion involves every student from a helper's perspective.

7. Gain a Commitment

Ask individuals to commit to the desired behavior. *Lifelines* accomplishes this through the help-seeking pledge and wallet card in session 4.

Remember, the objective of *Lifelines* is to help students to move from "I can handle this myself" to "This is a situation in which I need to turn to an adult for help." Students need to be given

- *opportunities* to (a) recognize a suicidal situation; (b) decide what to do about it; and (c) decide to seek help

- *skills* to (a) show their caring and concern; (b) ask about suicide; and (c) get help through identification of a helpful adult or other resource

- *recognition* for appropriate responses. Practice provides the involvement and the incorporation of the opportunities, skills, and recognition.

Part 2

Training for School Faculty and Staff

Training for School Faculty and Staff

....

DESCRIPTION

The following presentation is designed as an informational session on youth suicide for all school faculty and staff members. It reviews the reasons for the school's decision to address youth suicide prevention, introduces the *Lifelines* curriculum, explains the limited but critical role school staff play in the prevention process, and provides practical guidelines for their involvement.

The program is usually conducted by a member of the school's crisis resource/response team (social worker, psychologist, counseling staff) or by a health teacher familiar with the content. The presentation should be scheduled after the review of policies and procedures by school administration and prior to the first lesson for students. It is usually provided as part of an in-service day and may be presented more than once to accommodate the scheduling needs of all staff members. Because *Lifelines* is framed in the context of the "competent school community," it is extremely important to encourage attendance by all staff who interact with students, from administrative assistants to food service and maintenance staff.

This presentation is usually made in conjunction with the introduction of the *Lifelines* program into a school. However, it can also serve to educate the faculty of a school that is not using the entire *Lifelines* program.

The following program outline suggests one way of organizing and presenting this material for a 45- to 60-minute presentation. When time allows for participant discussion, the presentation may last one and one-half to two hours. Supplementary material is included for schools that choose to allocate additional time to this topic. While both the content and format of the meeting are flexible and can be

55

adjusted to the needs of individual schools, the emphasis should be on information that has practical implications for educators. Presentations that contain clinical or mental health jargon, theoretical concepts, or abstract statistics are generally not well received.

To be most effective, the delivery of this material should be adapted to the presenter's particular style of presentation.

OUTCOMES

By the end of the presentation, participants will be able to

- understand their role in the school's suicide prevention strategy
- better recognize students who may be at risk for suicide
- provide an effective initial response to these students
- understand how to refer students for further help

MATERIALS NEEDED

- Presentation outline (pages 57–69 of this manual)
- Handouts from CD-ROM:
    - Frequently Asked Questions about Youth Suicide **INTRO-2**
    - Warning Signs of Suicide **P2-1**
    - FACTS **P2-2**
- Copy of school policies and procedures for reference
- School Staff PowerPoint presentation from the CD-ROM
- *Not My Kid* DVD
- Laptop computer, LCD projector, screen, and external speakers if PowerPoint presentation and DVD are to be used

PREPARATION NEEDED

- Review the presentation outline and adjust the content to the time constraints of the program.
- Incorporate the PowerPoint slides if desired.
- Print and photocopy handouts, one per participant.
- Preview the DVD.

Presentation Outline

PART 1: WHY TALK ABOUT YOUTH SUICIDE?

How pervasive is the problem of youth suicide? Here's a brief review of what national data[1] tell us:

- It is the third-leading cause of death for teens.

- It is the second-leading cause of death among college students.

- For every death by suicide, there are between fifty and two hundred attempts.

- According to the 2007 Centers for Disease Control and Prevention Youth Risk Behavior Survey, 6.9 percent of students in grades nine through twelve reported an attempt in the past year; and 14.5 percent of high school students reported having thoughts about suicide.

- Attempts and suicide death rate are increasing for ten- to fourteen-year-olds.

But sometimes these percentages and survey results can simply seem like numbers and not communicate the reality of youth suicide to us in a personal way. So consider these numbers instead:

- Every year, there are approximately ten youth suicides for every 100,000 youth.

- Every day, there are approximately eleven youth suicides.

- Every two hours and eleven minutes, a person under the age of twenty-five dies by suicide.

The other part of the story—for which there really are no numbers—is the terrible impact on the family members and close friends of the deceased. That devastation is immeasurable.

(At this point in the presentation, you may choose to show the first two minutes and forty-five seconds of the Not My Kid *DVD, which includes parents Scott Fritz and Don Quigley talking about the suicide deaths of their children. This segment is powerful and evocative, and serves as a very clear reminder that youth suicide can happen in any family at any time. It is an effective training tool that engages the audience with the topic at an emotional level. This DVD was created by the Society for the Prevention of Teen Suicide.)*

Based on the number of you sitting in this room today, we know that some of *your* lives have been personally touched by the tragedy of suicide. It may have been in your friendship circle, your community, or your family. There are also some of you who have struggled with your own thoughts of suicide. And the students in our school are no different than you. Some of them will also have been impacted by suicide or suicidal behavior. That's one of the reasons that this program is so important—it acknowledges the personal reality of suicide and makes a statement that our school is committed to devoting time and resources to suicide prevention.

(If your school has experienced a suicide in the recent past, it is important to refer to that event and ask participants to share their recollections of the impact of that death.)

PART 2: DOES THE SCHOOL HAVE A ROLE IN SUICIDE PREVENTION?

The answer to that question is yes. It is a critical but limited one that recognizes that your primary role is to educate your students, not become their mental health clinicians. The role of the school in suicide prevention falls within the school's mandate to educate and protect its students and staff.

According to the Carnegie Task Force on Education, "School systems are not responsible for meeting every need of their students, but when the need directly affects learning, the school must meet the challenge."[2] The learning ability of children who are struggling with thoughts about suicide is obviously compromised.

Using the school as a focus for suicide prevention also does something else that's really important: it normalizes talking about suicide and reinforces the importance of asking for help. Students need to learn that it's okay and important to talk about difficult feelings with adults in their lives who can help them deal with those feelings. The learning environment of the school is designed to teach and emphasize those kinds of communication skills.

Another way to conceptualize the role of the school in the prevention of self-destructive behaviors for all students is to create and maintain what is called a "competent community." In a competent community, all members of the school are concerned about the welfare of each other and know how to come to each other's aid. Everyone, from the top administrator to the part-time bus driver, is dedicated to suicide prevention and engaged in activities to support this goal, which include:

- providing an effective initial response to kids exhibiting suicidal behavior (while not becoming professional counselors) and
- knowing where in the school to refer at-risk kids for further help

So what are the practical and specific ways schools can address these goals? Here are at least three important ways:

1. **Identification.** You spend more time with teens in a relatively structured environment than their parents do. You may be able to spot changes in a student that can indicate he or she is experiencing some trouble. For example, you may notice drops in performance, excessive misbehavior, fatigue, or someone who no longer cares about appearance.

2. **Support and Response.** Your contacts with students, particularly outside of classes, may enable you to have supportive relationships with them in which you can more readily notice problems or be approached by a student for help. You don't have to be a counselor to the students; you can simply provide a supportive initial response and get additional help for the student.

3. **Education.** Your role in this realm is the same as it is in all your other school activities: to instruct. All students need to know how to respond to troubled peers and what resources are available; and troubled students need to know available resources and preferable options.

Schools must provide the resources and competencies for helping everyone in the school to better recognize students who may be at risk for suicide. It's important to remember that you don't have to become experts in risk assessment. Your critical role is simply to recognize behaviors that may signal risk and to then refer these students for more comprehensive assessment by trained mental health professionals.

PART 3: HOW IS OUR SCHOOL ADDRESSING ITS ROLE IN YOUTH SUICIDE PREVENTION?

Our school has chosen the research- and evidence-based *Lifelines* program as a way of becoming a "competent community" and engaging the entire school in suicide prevention. The goal of *Lifelines* is to develop the school-based expertise and supports for responding to the problem of adolescent suicidal behavior. The objectives of the program are to increase the probability that persons who come into contact with potentially suicidal adolescents

- can more readily identify them
- know how to respond to them

- know how to rapidly obtain help for them

- will be consistently inclined to take such action

Another main objective of the *Lifelines* program is to make sure troubled adolescents are aware of and have access to helping resources so that they are inclined to seek help as an alternative to suicidal behavior.

Lifelines has four components:

1. **Administrative Readiness Consultation.** Our school's policies and procedures demonstrate commitment and support from the school's administrators and outline a prepared and planned response to students who might be at suicide risk. Our administrators have reviewed our school's policies prior to this presentation. *(Indicate how and where staff can access and review these policies.)*

2. **Faculty and Staff Training.** The next part of our competent school community consists of this presentation, which is being offered to all school employees. The goal is to ensure that anyone who interacts with students— no matter what their role in the school or how informal or unstructured their contact with students—will know some of the ways to identify students who may be at risk for suicide as well as exactly whom to contact to get help for students who may be at risk. Your role is fairly simple:

   - learning the warning signs of suicide

   - identifying at-risk students

   - referring at-risk students to appropriate resources

3. **Parent Workshop.** Parents also play a key role in the prevention process, which is why a workshop for parents is the third program component. It's designed to help parents understand why our school has decided to address this important topic and provide them with guidelines and resources for addressing suicide risk with their own kids.

4. **Student Curriculum.** The core of the *Lifelines* program is the curriculum. Students in *(give grade level)* will participate in a four-session unit that teaches them to

   - be aware of relevant facts about suicide, including warning signs

   - recognize the threat of suicidal thoughts and behavior and take troubled peers seriously

- respond in appropriate ways to troubled peers

- demonstrate positive attitudes about intervention and help-seeking behavior

- identify resources, be able to name one helpful adult, and know how resources will respond

PART 4: HOW CAN EDUCATORS ADDRESS THEIR ROLE IN SUICIDE PREVENTION?

Step 1: Answering Commonly Asked Questions

(Before beginning this section, distribute the Frequently Asked Questions about Youth Suicide handout.)

INTRO-2

The first step in the process is to separate fact from fiction by answering some of the most commonly asked questions about youth suicide:

Are School Programs That Discuss Suicide Safe?

Systematic school programs for suicide prevention were first put into place in the 1980s. Evaluation research done at that time cautioned against talking about suicide in the classroom in ways that glamorized or sensationalized the topic or made it seem like a normal solution to life problems and stresses. Some people misinterpreted that message to mean that all school-based programs that address suicide were potentially dangerous, and there has been a lot of confusion about whether suicide prevention programs actually encourage suicide. We have since learned, according to the Centers for Disease Control and Prevention, that students do, in fact, benefit from programs that present suicide in a factual way.

Can Talking about Suicide Plant the Idea in the Minds of Vulnerable Teens?

No. Whether or not we like to admit it, as the earlier statistics have demonstrated, suicide is a tragic reality in the lives of our students. If you were to go into any high school classroom and ask the students if they know anyone who has attempted or completed suicide, over 75 percent of them would respond affirmatively. Suicide is a frequent topic in the media and is one of the most significant public health problems of our time. Talking about suicide provides an opportunity to address stigma and correct misinformation. The issue is not whether suicide should be talked about, but *how* it is treated as a topic for discussion. The *Lifelines* curriculum, which is based on the research about the most effective classroom interventions, focuses on helping students recognize the signs of risk in peers, identify ways they can express their concerns, and talk to adults about their concerns. Because research has also shown that adolescents are often reluctant to talk with school-based adults about their concerns, the curriculum focuses on helping students realize that adults in their school *can* be resources, and encourages them to identify at least one adult in the school to whom they would be willing to turn.

Is Talking about Suicide Just a Way for Someone to Get Attention?

If a student talks about suicide as a way to get attention, then you're dealing with a youth whose problem-solving skills are underdeveloped. For most students and adults, suicide isn't a socially acceptable way to solve problems or get attention. Some students may "talk" about suicide indirectly, through their writing or artwork. Pay attention to these types of communications from your students and ask about anything that gets your attention, especially if it is out of the developmental norm or is particularly violent. Not every inquiry will need follow-up, but if you hear an answer that concerns you, keep your eyes open for other signs of suicide risk. Don't make assumptions about a student's degree of seriousness based on how often or how casually suicide threats are made. *Every threat should be taken seriously.* For example, if any student is overheard talking about suicide, whether or not the threat is perceived as serious, your school's resource staff should be consulted immediately.

(Discuss any questions participants have regarding the Frequently Asked Questions about Youth Suicide handout.)

Step 2: Understanding the Characteristics of Suicide

The next step is to define suicide. While the simplistic explanation "taking one's own life" is accurate, it doesn't do much for us in a practical way. So what do you know about facing someone who is suicidal? Here are some helpful facts:

(If you are short on time, go through the following three bullet points. If you have more time, skip to the expanded version of step 2 on pages 63–65.)

- Most suicidal people are thinking about suicide as the solution to a problem they can't figure out how to solve by any other means. The question isn't why they want to die but what's going on in their lives right now that has them thinking that death is the only way out.

- Suicidal thinking is crisis thinking. That is, it is often irrational, ambivalent, emotional, and confused. Simply listening to what suicidal people are saying in a calm, nonjudgmental way helps to bring them back to reality. Just letting someone talk can often defuse emotional intensity.

- Suicide is often considered as a means of communication. The suicidal person is trying to send a message to someone with the suicide attempt. A helpful, simple question that gets at this point is, "To whom do you want your suicide attempt to send a message and what is the message you want to send?"[3]

(The following is an expanded version of step 2: Understanding the Characteristics of Suicide and may be substituted if time permits. If time does not permit, skip to step 3: Identifying Risk Factors, Warning Signs, and Protective Factors on page 65.)

a. **Suicide is an alternative.** Viewing suicide from this perspective has several important implications. For one, just as a teen may feel a temporary high from a drug, he or she may obtain temporary attention, support, or even popularity after a suicide attempt. These positive effects are short lived, however, if the basic problems that underlie the attempt aren't addressed. And again, as with drugs, there is tremendous risk of death or permanent disability associated with using a suicide attempt as a way of coping. A second implication of viewing suicide as an alternative is that suicide can then be understood as less a wish to die than a wish to escape the intense emotional pain generated from what appears to be an inescapable situation. The most relevant question is "What's going on in your life right now that has you feeling so terrible that you think death is the only answer?"

b. **Crisis thinking colors problem solving.** A crisis may be thought of as any situation in which we feel that our skills do not meet the demands of the environment. In this regard, we realize that crises can be frequent visitors in our lives. And we also realize that most of us do not do our best problem solving in crisis situations. People in crisis, especially suicidal crisis, describe themselves as feeling as if they are in a tunnel and there's no way out except suicide. Adolescents are particularly susceptible to this anxiety and tunnel thinking when confronted with a crisis, because they do not have the life experiences of having worked their way through difficult situations. So our job as adults is to open up that tunnel, help the person see the problem in a different way, and come up with alternatives. Sometimes by just talking about a problem, a person's level of anxiety and hopelessness can diminish and problem-solving skills can open up again.

(Depending on the size of the group, you may want to do a short experiential exercise. Ask participants to think of the last time they experienced a personal crisis and to share their reactions to the crisis, not the specific situation that generated the crisis. Summarize responses, and then inquire about what strategies people use to cope in crisis. The responses you receive will include "talking with someone." Ask participants to describe the characteristics of the person to whom they turn for help in a crisis. The list will invariably include characteristics such as nonjudgmental, a good listener, doesn't solve the problem for me. Remind participants that these are the same qualities that students find helpful when they are having crises in their lives. Once we have the opportunity to talk through the situation that's troubling us, we often experience a decrease in the intensity of feelings surrounding it and problem-solving skills become less compromised.)

c. **Person is often ambivalent.** This means that the person is feeling two things at the same time: a part of the person wants to die and a part wants to live. When talking with a suicidal student, we must acknowledge both of these feelings. While we line up with and unequivocally support the side that wants to live, this can't be done by ignoring or dismissing the side that wants to die. Think about times in your life when you've had a strong feeling and someone close to you ignores it or tells you that you don't really feel that way. This response probably only made you feel misunderstood and unsupported and may have permanently shut down communication. Acknowledging that there is a part of the person that really wants to die and letting the person talk about it may be scary, but doing so will lower the person's anxiety. Ignoring those feelings or discounting them can raise anxiety and increase the feelings of isolation that are so prevalent in people who are feeling suicidal.

d. **Suicidal solution has an irrational component.** People who are suicidal are often unaware of the consequences of suicide that are obvious to the rest of the world. For example, they are usually not thinking about the impact of their death on others, or they hold a perception that they will be reincarnated or somehow still be present to see how others react to their death. This irrationality reflects how trapped and helpless the person feels. In these situations it is usually more helpful to talk rationally about the reasons the person may have for living rather than try to address the irrationality about dying.

e. **Suicide is a form of communication.** For people who are suicidal, normal communication has usually broken down, and the suicide attempt may be the person's way of sending a message or reacting to the isolation he or she feels because his or her communication skills are ineffective. The question that addresses this breakdown can be phrased in the following way: "To whom do you want your suicide attempt to send a message to and what do you want that message to be?"

So in summary, many suicides are attempts to resolve problems or escape from situations by a person who is in crisis, may be ambivalent, and can't see any other alternative. This person has usually become increasingly emotionally isolated from others and, in his or her crisis state, has not necessarily thought through the consequences of this alternative.

Step 3: Identifying Risk Factors, Warning Signs, and Protective Factors

Now that we have a shared understanding of the characteristics of suicide, the next step is to identify risk factors, warning signs, and protective factors for youth suicide. One way to conceptualize the differences in suicide risk factors and warning signs is to use the model of a traffic signal.

Risk Factors

Consider the risk factors as the "yellow light" that tells us we need to slow down and pay attention, and the warning signs as the "red light" that signals we need to stop immediately. There is also a "green light" to consider—these are protective factors that buffer a person against suicide risk. Let's review each of these separately. Please note that risk factors do not cause suicide nor do they predict suicide. They simply place people at higher risk for suicide.

(For more complete information, see the Youth Suicide Fact Sheet found at www.suicidology. org. Depending on time constraints, frame discussion around any of these risk factors.)

- Risk factors include demographic factors such as age, race, and sexual orientation. In the fifteen- to twenty-four-year-old age bracket, white males ages eighteen to nineteen have the highest suicide rates and African American females have the lowest. The suicide rates for youth ages ten to fourteen increased dramatically between 1981 and 2004 (51 percent). We know that gay and lesbian youth are at increased risk, although the extent is still not clear and research into this risk factor is continuing. *(For more information, check out www.sprc.org/library/SPRC_LGBT_Youth.pdf.)*

- Additional risk factors include

  - a psychiatric history or drug and/or alcohol abuse. One of the most serious risk factors is a previous suicide attempt, especially when it is combined with other risk factors.

- a family history that includes physical or sexual abuse as well as a family history that includes suicide

- exposure to another's suicide, even if it is through media reports

- In combination with these other factors, the experience of stressful life events can also increase risk.

- Certain personality factors can also elevate risk. Students who are impulsive, immature, or anxious worriers tend to have the poor judgment and underdeveloped problem-solving skills that can increase risk. We also need to be concerned about kids who display aggressive behavior, especially outbursts of rage.

- Access to means is the most preventive risk factor. A study in Illinois determined that removing access to lethal means, especially guns, was effective in lowering the rate of youth suicides.[4] Removing access to over-the-counter acetaminophen is also recommended, since this drug is one of the most common medications used in overdoses among young adolescents.

As you review these risk factors, of course, you may recognize their presence in many of the students in our school. It is true that they are not uncommon. They become dangerous when they exist in combination.

Some of these risk factors are "fixed" or unchangeable—like family history, for example. Others, like access to means, are considered "variable" and can be changed. By eliminating variable factors, the risk for suicide can be temporarily lowered.

One of the most effective ways to lower risk is to recognize when students are at elevated risk and get them to a resource person. The resource person can then assist them in developing more permanent risk-reduction strategies.

Warning Signs

(Before discussing this section, distribute the Warning Signs of Suicide and FACTS handouts.)

 P2-1, P2-2

The "red lights" on the traffic light are the warning signs: the things that make us stop in our tracks. The word "FACTS" provides a helpful acrostic for identifying these red lights or warning signs. *(Discuss the handouts.)*

Remember that this is not a foolproof set of indicators for suicide. Except for the category of "Threats," they may just indicate that a student is troubled, but troubled students are more likely to think about suicide. If you do come across a student who has made a threat, no matter how vague, or who gives you the sense through conversation, class work, or behavior that he or she is thinking about suicide, refer that student immediately to your resource staff member for additional assessment.

If you don't have a sense of immediacy created by a specific threat or ideation, what do you do if you identify other warning signs in your students? Share your concerns with colleagues. By comparing notes with other teachers, staff, or administrators, you may get a more complete picture that will either calm your concerns or make a case for taking action. The action you take *always* involves going to the appropriate person designated in your policy. Don't be afraid of making mistakes— overreacting is *always* better than underreacting.

If you feel comfortable, you can also talk with the student about your concerns. Be specific. "I'm worried about you" should include the *why*—"because your grades are slipping, you seem distracted in class, you've stopped turning in homework." Be sure to mention the specifics that gave rise to your concerns. When approaching an at-risk student, follow these steps:

- *Listen to the student's responses.*

  - Acknowledge feelings in the student's terms ("It sounds like you've been feeling stressed lately and you just don't care about school anymore.")

  - Clarify what you hear ("Can you tell me what 'not caring about school' means?")

  - Summarize ("So the last few weeks have been hard for you and you don't even care anymore if you graduate although you're not really sure why.")

  - Validate ("Well, your schoolwork shows that you certainly haven't been your old self lately and I'm concerned to hear that you feel like giving up on school.")

- *Know your limits.* Remember you don't need to know all the details behind the student's distress. Your role is simply to identify students with warning signs and either to consult with our school resource staff member about the next step or to refer the student to them for further assessment. In most cases, you do not need to ask about suicide directly. But if the student raises the topic, it's important to respond with concern. Don't minimize ("Oh, come on, you'd never do something like that!") or overreact ("You should be in a hospital, not in a school!"). Simply acknowledge the seriousness of the situation, express your plan or intention to get the student to someone who can help him or her with these feelings, and escort the student to the person in our school designated to make further assessment. Tell the student that often the hardest part of help-seeking is the first step: admitting to yourself that you're struggling with something you can't handle on your own. Once a student can admit this, the door to getting help is opened. Your job is to escort the student to the next step.

- *Know your resources.* Be clear about your school's resources and the procedures for referring at-risk students before you need to use them.

- *Follow up.* Keep the student on your radar screen and check in periodically. A simple but genuine "How are you doing?" and "Is there anything I can do to help you out?" are often enough.

Protective Factors

Suicide risk is balanced by what we talked about earlier as the "green lights," or protective factors.

Protective factors are just that: personal, behavioral, or situational characteristics that contribute to a student's resiliency and buffer him or her against factors that can increase risk. One of the most significant protective factors for youth is a caring relationship with a trusted adult. For many youth, that person is a teacher.

Other protections include

- a sense of connection or participation in school

- positive self-esteem and good coping skills

- access to care for emotional or physical problems or for substance abuse disorders

- cultural or religious beliefs that discourage suicide and promote self-preservation

A school that truly functions as a competent community is actually in the position to foster the development of protective factors in its student population. For example, students can be helped to identify trusted adults in their lives, and encouraged to participate in school and community activities. They can also be taught, as some current school suicide prevention programs emphasize, that it's courageous to ask for help, a very important concept for adolescent boys in particular. Students' efforts in school can be acknowledged, something that is critical for students who are marginal performers. Lastly, and perhaps both the easiest and hardest thing for educators to do, is to be a good listener to both verbal and non-verbal student communication, as often as possible.

PART 5: THE PROCEDURES IN YOUR SCHOOL

(Briefly review the procedures in your school for identifying and referring students who might be at suicide risk. Even if it may seem redundant, name the specific staff members who are available to talk with faculty and staff about students and to whom referrals are to be made. If your school has a specific procedure for providing limited feedback on these referrals, review that as well.)

PART 6: SUMMARY: PUTTING IT ALL TOGETHER

So what's the take-away from this? No student, faculty or staff member, administrator, parent, or school should have to deal with suicidal behavior alone. By developing an informed, supportive, and organized "competent community" that is backed up by cooperative community mental health and health resources, it is possible to provide an effective response to troubled teens, their families, and friends.

This brief workshop has provided critical but limited information. Additional information on suicide and the prevention of suicide can be found at the following Web sites:

- Society for the Prevention of Teen Suicide: www.sptsnj.org
- Suicide Prevention Resource Center: www.sprc.org
- American Foundation for Suicide Prevention: www.afsp.org
- American Association of Suicidology: www.suicidology.org
- Maine Youth Suicide Prevention Program: www.maine.gov/suicide
- Maine Teen Suicide Prevention: www.maine.gov/suicide/youth

Part 3

Parent Workshop

Parent Workshop

....

DESCRIPTION

This 45- to 60-minute presentation is designed to increase awareness of youth suicide for parents. If time permits discussion, the presentation may last one to one and one-half hours. Parents will be introduced to the *Lifelines* program and goals, and they will learn basic information about addressing the topic of suicide with their children.

The presentation is usually conducted by a member of the school's crisis resource (or response) team, which may include a social worker, psychologist, counseling staff member, or health teacher familiar with the content. School officials should attend the meeting as well.

This presentation should be held prior to implementing the student curriculum. It is usually provided in conjunction with a school's parent-teacher organization or other community organization or group that can engage parent participation. Because parental attendance is often challenging, this presentation can be repeated in order to reach a greater number of parents.

The following outline suggests one way of organizing and presenting the material to parents. Both the content and format of the meeting, however, are flexible and can be adjusted to the needs of individual schools. It may also be helpful to adapt the content and include the parent handouts on your school's Web site.

OUTCOMES

By the end of the presentation, participants will be able to

- describe the prevalence of youth suicide
- define reasons for the school's decision to present a student unit on suicide prevention
- identify at least three topics covered in the *Lifelines* student curriculum
- explain how discussing suicide does not plant the idea in anyone's mind
- list at least four guidelines for talking about suicide with their children

MATERIALS NEEDED

- Presentation outline (pages 75–80 of this manual)
- Handouts from CD-ROM:
    - Frequently Asked Questions for Parents 🖥 **P3-1** (SP)
    - Starting the Conversation 🖥 **P3-2** (SP)
    - FACTS 🖥 **P3-3** (SP)
    - Addressing Worrisome Behaviors 🖥 **P3-4** (SP)
    - What Can Parents Do? 🖥 **P3-5** (SP)
- Parent PowerPoint presentation from the CD-ROM
- *Not My Kid* DVD
- Laptop computer, LCD projector, screen, and external speakers if PowerPoint presentation and DVD are to be used
- List of local mental health resources

PREPARATION NEEDED

- Decide on the venue. Consider the anticipated attendance when you select a location. For a small group, a classroom or library generally facilitates more participation than a larger space like an auditorium or cafeteria.
- Advertise the program. Select a title that will grab parent interest and emphasize the positive impact of the curriculum. Consider something like "*Lifelines:* A Program for Raising Resilient Kids." Because suicide still carries a social stigma, experience has shown that incorporating the word "suicide" into the title can discourage attendance. Many parents, unfortunately,

continue to hold the mind-set of "not my child!" and would not consider a program on youth suicide to be relevant.

- Create a list of local mental health resources. This list should include private practitioners as well as public agencies and hospitals that provide suicide risk assessment and counseling services. Make a copy for each participant.

- Review the presentation outline. Incorporate the PowerPoint slides and video clips if desired.

- Print and photocopy handouts, one per participant.

- Preview the DVD.

Presentation Outline

PART 1: WHY TALK ABOUT YOUTH SUICIDE?

One of the most effective ways to begin this training is to show the first two minutes and forty-five seconds of the Not My Kid *DVD, which includes two parents describing how stunned they were after the deaths of their children by suicide. They explain that they felt like it could never happen to them. Using this segment to begin the workshop immediately establishes the reality of youth suicide that dry statistics can never convey.*

We teach our kids about seat-belt safety; to stop, drop, and roll in case of fire; about the dangers of drug and alcohol use; and about safe sex practices. Yet we often do not address the third-leading cause of death in our youth after accidents and homicides. This is youth suicide.

Youth suicide is a quiet secret that takes the lives of over five thousand of America's youth each year. But five thousand is a large number that in some ways masks the more personal impact of a death by suicide. Let's break that number down into figures that are a bit easier to understand.

- Every year, there are approximately ten youth suicides for every 100,000 youth.

- Every day, there are approximately eleven youth suicides.

- Every two hours and eleven minutes, a person under the age of twenty-five completes suicide.[1]

These numbers tell only part of the story. Experts estimate that for every suicide death there are between fifty and two hundred attempts. Why is there such a difference in these estimates? One reason is that there is still so much social stigma about reporting a death as a suicide that it is often recorded as accidental.[2]

These numbers, however, are what experts tell us. What do our kids tell us? Every year the Centers for Disease Control and Prevention conducts a Youth Risk Behavior Survey in which high school students are asked a number of health-related questions. Let's take a look at what kids reported about suicide in the year 2007:

- 6.9 percent of students in grades nine through twelve reported an attempt in the past year.

- 14.5 percent of high school students reported suicidal thoughts or ideation.[3]

(You may also incorporate your state statistics about youth suicide. You can find this information at www.sprc.org or from the Youth Risk Behavior Survey at www.cdc.gov/ HealthyYouth/yrbs/index.htm. Just remember, current numbers are generally not available because there is often a delay of up to two years in data analysis.)

What we take away from this is that our kids *are* challenged by thoughts and feelings about suicide and that we as their parents and caretakers in their lives need to be better prepared to deal with this disturbing reality. And because kids spend the greatest amount of their time in schools, one of the easiest ways to integrate learning about suicide prevention into the lives of our children is in the educational setting.

P3-1 (SP)   *(Distribute the Frequently Asked Questions for Parents handout and briefly discuss.)*

PART 2: DOES THE SCHOOL HAVE A ROLE IN SUICIDE PREVENTION?

Yes—the role is a critical but limited one. According to the Carnegie Task Force on Education, "School systems are not responsible for meeting every need of their students, but when the need directly affects learning, the school must meet the challenge."[4] The learning ability of children who are struggling with thoughts about suicide is obviously compromised.

Using the school as a focus for suicide prevention does something else that's really important: it normalizes talking about suicide and reinforces the importance of asking for help. Our children need to learn that it's okay and important to talk about distressing or overwhelming feelings with adults in their lives who can help them deal with these feelings. The learning environment of the school is designed to teach and emphasize those kinds of communication skills. The school is also in a unique position to reinforce "protective factors" that can buffer students from some of the risk factors for suicide.

PART 3: HOW IS OUR SCHOOL ADDRESSING ITS ROLE IN YOUTH SUICIDE PREVENTION?

Our school has chosen the *Lifelines* program as a way of engaging the entire school community in suicide prevention. The first objective of *Lifelines* is to increase the likelihood that those who come into contact with potentially suicidal adolescents can:

- readily identify them

- know how to respond

- know how to quickly get help

- always be ready to take such action

The second objective is to provide troubled youth with an awareness of and access to resources that can help them.

Lifelines has four components:

1. **Administrative Readiness Consultation.** Our school's commitment to youth suicide prevention began at the top administrative level with a review of policies and procedures for responding to at-risk students.

2. **Faculty and Staff Training.** All school staff members have attended an in-service training to help them identify students who might be at risk for suicide, to review strategies for approaching these students, and to identify in-school referral resources.

3. **Parent Workshop.** You also play a key role in the prevention process. This workshop is designed to help you understand why our school has decided to address this important topic, and to provide you with guidelines and resources for addressing suicide risk with your own kids.

4. **Student Curriculum.** Students in *(specify grade)* will participate in a four-session unit that will be taught by one of their regular teachers who has received training in the curriculum implementation. This is an important feature of the *Lifelines* program, which is designed to increase both the capacity of school staff to respond to students at risk of suicide, and the perception of students that staff are approachable if they need help. The curriculum, which includes activities and a DVD, teaches students

   - relevant facts about suicide, including warning signs

- how to recognize the threat of suicidal thoughts and behavior and take troubled peers seriously

- how to respond to troubled peers

- to demonstrate positive attitudes about intervention and help-seeking behavior

- what resources are available

- to be able to name one helpful adult and know how resources will respond

PART 4: HOW CAN PARENTS ADDRESS THEIR ROLE IN SUICIDE PREVENTION?

Talking with your children about suicide is as important as talking about drugs and alcohol and safe driving. A common and unfortunate myth about suicide is that talking about it can plant the idea in someone's mind. Not only is this false but it is also dangerous. Keeping thoughts and feelings about suicide a secret does nothing to address their dangerousness or root out the reason behind them. Giving your kids permission to talk about suicide opens up an important area of communication. Suicide is, in fact, often referred to as a "crisis of communication." People who struggle with thoughts or feelings about suicide report that they are often afraid to bring up the subject. By opening up the conversation, you model how suicide *can* be talked about and reinforce your availability as a supportive resource when your child is having a hard time.

 P3-2 (SP)

(Distribute the Starting the Conversation handout.)

So how do you start this conversation? Here are some suggestions:

- **Pick a good time.** You want your child's full attention, so choose a time when there are minimal distractions and a reasonable degree of privacy.

- **Be conversational.** Remember that your goal is to have a conversation with your child, not deliver a lecture. It always helps to have a "reference point," such as an event or a news story or the school's *Lifelines* classes, to start the conversation. ("I was reading in the newspaper that the rate of suicide for teens has increased . . ." or "I noticed on the school's Web site that the school is having a suicide prevention workshop for the teachers . . .")

- **Be honest.** If this is a hard subject for you to talk about, acknowledge it. ("You know, I never thought I'd be talking with you about suicide. It's a topic I've never been really comfortable with . . .") By acknowledging your discomfort, you give you child permission to acknowledge his or her discomfort, too.

- **Be direct.** Ask open-ended questions to clarify your child's responses. ("Tell me how you feel talking about suicide." "What do you think about suicide?" "What have you learned about suicide in school?")

- **Listen to what your child has to say.** You've brought up the topic. You're interested in his or her responses, so simply listen to your child's answers. Don't interrupt or interject your opinion unless asked.

- **If you hear something that worries you, ask for more information.** ("You say that one of your friends has talked about suicide. Tell me more.")

- **Open the door to revisit the conversation.** Suicide isn't a one-time discussion topic. Once you've made it okay to talk about, it should be easier to bring up again. If you've heard something that concerns you, make sure to ask about it again.

PART 5: SHOULD YOU WORRY ABOUT YOUR CHILD?

Experts have identified warning signs of suicide that might indicate a child is at risk. While this list is in no way exhaustive, it does identify specific categories that are important to remember. They are organized around the word FACTS.

(Distribute the FACTS and Addressing Worrisome Behaviors handouts. Read through the FACTS handout first. Explain that this handout is part of the student curriculum. The Addressing Worrisome Behaviors handout is discussed below.)

(SP) P3-3, P3-4

If certain behaviors concern you, it's important to take these concerns seriously. Here are guidelines to follow when addressing worrisome behaviors:

- **Don't worry about overreacting.** Sit with your child and let him or her know about your concerns. ("You said something that worries me." or "You don't seem to be yourself lately.")

- **Be specific about your concerns.** ("I've noticed you aren't spending as much time with your friends and you seem annoyed when they call you." or "You spend hours doing your homework, but every time I check on you, you're just staring into space." or "Your teacher called and said you're failing English because you're late to class almost every day.")

- **Expect your child to discount your concerns.** ("All the kids are having trouble getting homework finished." or "My friends are annoying." or "That teacher fails everybody.") Explain that you're not concerned about everybody in the class. You are concerned about your child. Be prepared to offer more than one example; the more evidence you have, the harder it will be for your child to minimize your examples.

- **If your child says anything that even hints at thoughts of suicide, ask about it.** For example, statements like "Sometimes I'm not sure life is worth living." or "I just can't take it much more." *must* be explored further. *You cannot plant the idea of suicide in your child's mind by asking about it!* In asking about thoughts of suicide, you open up the lines of communication as well as introduce the idea of help-seeking by asking to hear more about your child's distressing thoughts.

- **Act immediately if you have concerns about suicide.** Get your child to a mental health professional as soon as possible for an evaluation. There are several ways to do this.

(Distribute the list of local resources you have generated and review them briefly.)

Whatever resource you choose, indicate the urgency of the situation. Make sure to use the phrase "at risk for suicide." ("I'm concerned that my son may be at risk for suicide and I'd like to schedule an evaluation as soon as possible.") Although the evaluation might determine that your child is not at immediate risk for suicide, this is an assessment you'd like to have made quickly, and it is a decision that is best left to a trained mental health professional.

(If time permits, show the remainder of the Not My Kid *DVD.)*

PART 6: CONCLUSION

As parents, your role in suicide prevention is crucial. You know your child's moods and behaviors better than anyone else. If you see behavior that concerns you, ask your child about it. And be sure your child knows that he or she can feel comfortable about coming to you for help. Reiterate that you are there to listen and not to judge, and that you are there for your child, no matter what he or she has to say.

An excellent resource that demonstrates some of the questions you might want to ask a mental health professional as well as how to ask those questions is the video we watched today called *Not My Kid*. It was created by the Society for the Prevention of Teen Suicide and is available online at www.sptsnj.org.

P3-5 (SP)

(Distribute the What Can Parents Do? handout and encourage parents and guardians to read through the suggestions.)

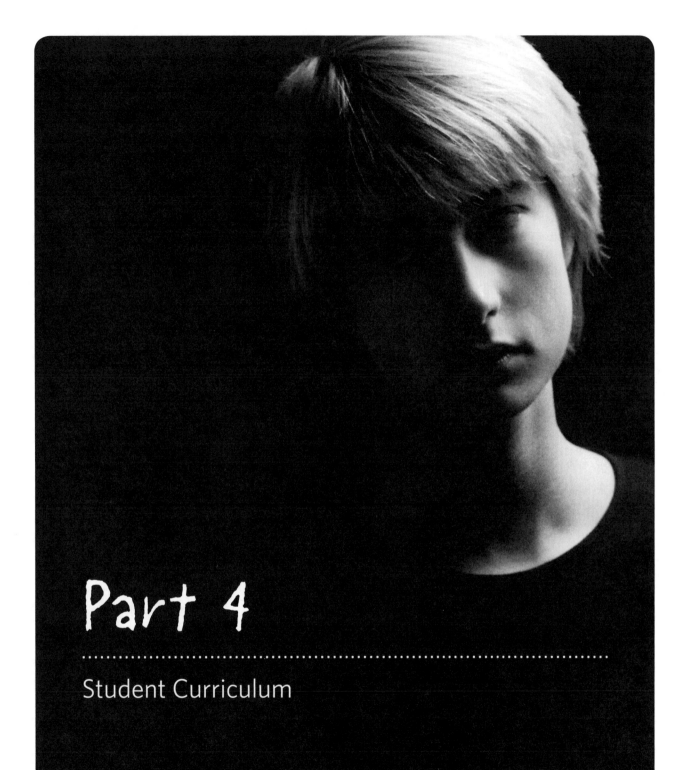

Part 4

Student Curriculum

Scope and Sequence

By the end of each session, students will be able to do the following:

Session 1: When Is a Friend in Trouble?	Session 2: How Do I Help a Friend?	Session 3: Where Can I Go to Get Help?	Session 4: How Can I Use What I've Learned?
• define reasons for a unit on suicide • examine personal reactions to a situation involving a peer's suicidal behavior • examine the ways in which our feelings about suicide influence our actions • identify basic facts about suicide	• recognize specific warning signs of suicide in themselves and others • organize warning signs around the FACTS sheet • name three basic suicide intervention steps • identify the words to use to ask about suicide	• discuss more fully how to implement the steps of a successful peer intervention • define traits of helpful people • identify school resources and procedures for responding to suicidal students	• demonstrate ability to help a troubled friend through scripted role-plays • demonstrate willingness to help self or a troubled friend by signing a help-seeking pledge • identify the wallet card as a resource

Related National Academic Standards[1]

Students in grades six through eight will

- Analyze the relationship between healthy behaviors and personal health.

- Describe the interrelationships of emotional, intellectual, physical, and social health in adolescence.

- Describe ways to reduce or prevent injuries and other adolescent health problems.

- Examine the likelihood of injury or illness if engaging in unhealthy behaviors.

- Examine the potential seriousness of injury or illness if engaging in unhealthy behaviors.

- Describe how peers influence healthy and unhealthy behaviors.

- Analyze how the school and community can affect personal health practices and behaviors.

- Determine the accessibility of products that enhance health.

- Describe situations that may require professional health services.

- Locate valid and reliable health products and services.

- Apply effective verbal and nonverbal communication skills to enhance health.

- Demonstrate refusal or negotiation skills that avoid or reduce health risks.

- Demonstrate effective conflict management or resolution strategies.

- Demonstrate how to ask for assistance to enhance the health of self or others.

- Identify circumstances that can help or hinder healthy decision making.

- Determine when health-related situations require the application of a thoughtful decision-making process.

- Distinguish when individual or collaborative decision making is appropriate.

- Distinguish between healthy and unhealthy alternatives to health-related issues or problems.

- Predict the potential short-term impact of each alternative on self or others.

- Analyze the outcomes of a health-related decision.

- Demonstrate healthy practices and behaviors that will maintain or improve the health of self and others.

- Demonstrate behaviors that avoid or reduce health risks to self and others.

- State a health-enhancing position on a topic and support it with accurate information.

- Demonstrate how to influence and support others to make positive health choices.

- Work cooperatively to advocate for healthy individuals, families, and schools.

Students in grades nine through twelve will

- Predict how healthy behaviors can affect health status.

- Describe the interrelationships of emotional, intellectual, physical, and social health.

- Propose ways to reduce or prevent injuries and health problems.

- Analyze the relationship between access to health care and health status.

- Analyze personal susceptibility to injury, illness, or death if engaging in unhealthy behaviors.

- Analyze the potential severity of injury or illness if engaging in unhealthy behaviors.

- Analyze how peers influence healthy and unhealthy behaviors.

- Evaluate how the school and community can affect personal health practices and behaviors.

- Evaluate the validity of health information, products, and services.

- Determine the accessibility of products and services that enhance health.

- Determine when professional health services may be required.

- Access valid and reliable health products and services.

- Use skills for communicating effectively with family, peers, and others to enhance health.

- Demonstrate refusal, negotiation, and collaboration skills to enhance health and avoid or reduce health risks.

- Demonstrate strategies to prevent, manage, or resolve interpersonal conflicts without harming self or others.

- Demonstrate how to ask for and offer assistance to enhance the health of self or others.

- Examine barriers that can hinder healthy decision making.

- Determine the value of applying a thoughtful decision-making process in health-related situations.

- Justify when individual or collaborative decision making is appropriate.

- Generate alternatives to health-related issues or problems.

- Predict the potential short-term and long-term impact of each alternative on self and others.

- Defend the healthy choice when making decisions.

- Evaluate the effectiveness of health-related decisions.

- Demonstrate a variety of healthy practices and behaviors that will maintain or improve the health of self and others.

- Demonstrate a variety of behaviors that avoid or reduce health risks to self and others.

- Demonstrate how to influence and support others to make positive health choices.

- Work cooperatively as an advocate for improving personal, family, and community health.

Session Descriptions and Preparation

Session Title	Session Description	Materials Needed	Preparation Needed
Session 1: When Is a Friend in Trouble?	Through classroom discussion and a brief quiz, students will learn accurate and relevant information about youth suicide. A classroom exercise that explores feelings about responding to a suicidal friend introduces the concept of help-seeking and the danger of keeping suicidal confidences.	• Handout: What Would You Do? • Handout: Questionnaire: True or False? • Posterboard and markers • Large clock if one is not available in the classroom • Board or flipchart and markers	1. Read the session outline. 2. Print and photocopy handouts, one per student. 3. Using posterboard and a marker, list the ground rules you would like students to follow when discussing this sensitive topic. Post the ground rules where all students can see them.
Session 2: How Do I Help a Friend?	Through discussion guided by a handout and DVD scenarios, students will begin to explore specific intervention steps to use when responding to suicidal friends. An additional handout will help them identify suicide warning signs.	• Board or flipchart and markers • DVD player and monitor • *A Teen's Guide to Suicide Prevention* video from the *Lifelines* DVD • Handout: Warning Signs of Suicide/FACTS • Handout: *A Teen's Guide to Suicide Prevention* Discussion Guidelines • Handout: Helpful Steps to Prevent Suicide	1. Read the session outline. 2. Print and photocopy handouts, one per student. 3. Set up the DVD player and monitor. 4. Post the ground rules from session 1, if they aren't still up.

Session Title	Session Description	Materials Needed	Preparation Needed
Session 3: Where Can I Go to Get Help?	Students will view the dramatization of a real-life suicide intervention undertaken by three students in Maine, using the skills they learned in the *Lifelines* curriculum. Through a classroom activity, students will identify the qualities of helpful people. Discussion will also review in-school and community resources.	• *One Life Saved: The Story of a Suicide Intervention* video from the *Lifelines* DVD • DVD player and monitor • Handout: Warning Signs of Suicide/FACTS • Handout: *One Life Saved* Discussion Questions • Handout: The Qualities of Helpful People • (Optional) Handout on school procedure for responding to suicidal students • Board or flipchart and markers • Chart paper with questions for discussion • Masking tape • Homework assignments for selected students (role-play scripts from session 4)	1. Read the session outline. 2. Select discussion questions for the part 2 activity (see part 2, step 6 of outline). Using the chart paper, write one question at the top of each sheet of paper, making sure to have two or three questions/sheets of paper per group. Cut strips of masking tape. 3. Print and photocopy handouts, one per student. 4. Set up DVD player and monitor. 5. Post the ground rules from session 1, if they aren't still up. 6. Preparation for session 4: Read the role-plays for session 4 and select two or three for class discussion. Each role-play will require two actors and a moderator. Choose three students for each role-play.

Session Title	Session Description	Materials Needed	Preparation Needed
Session 4: How Can I Use What I've Learned?	Session 4 uses scripted role-plays to practice intervening in suicidal behavior. A help-seeking pledge further commits students to taking action for themselves and others, and also clarifies the limits of their responsibility. A wallet card serves as a review and a resource.	• Board or flipchart and markers • Handout: Role-Play Scenarios (for actors and moderators) • Handout: Role-Play Discussion • Handout: Warning Signs of Suicide/FACTS • Handout: Help-Seeking Pledge • Handout: *Lifelines* Wallet Card	1. Prior to class, check in with the students you selected to participate in the role-plays to make sure they are prepared. Make extra copies of the role-plays in case they have forgotten to bring the copies you gave them at the last class session. 2. Review the instructions for the role-plays. 3. Print and photocopy handouts, one for each student. 4. Copy/create the wallet cards. 5. Post the ground rules from session 1, if they aren't still up.

When Is a Friend in Trouble?

....

DESCRIPTION

Through classroom discussion and a brief quiz, students will learn accurate and relevant information about youth suicide. A classroom exercise that explores feelings about responding to a suicidal friend introduces the concept of help-seeking and the danger of keeping suicidal confidences.

LEARNER OUTCOMES

By the end of the session, students will be able to

- define reasons for a unit on suicide

- examine personal reactions to a situation involving a peer's suicidal behavior

- examine the ways in which our feelings about suicide influence our actions

- identify basic facts about suicide

MATERIALS NEEDED

- Handouts from CD-ROM:
    - What Would You Do? 🖨 **S1-1**
    - Questionnaire: True or False? 🖨 **S1-2**
- Posterboard and markers

89

- Large clock if one is not available in the classroom
- Board or flipchart and markers

PREPARATION NEEDED

- Read the session outline.
- Print and photocopy handouts, one per student.
- Using posterboard and a marker, list the ground rules you would like students to follow when discussing this sensitive topic. Post the ground rules where all students can see them. Sample rules: confidentiality (what is said here, stays here), listen when someone is talking/no side conversations, no joking around, use respectful language, no criticism of others' ideas.

Session 1 Outline

PART 1
8 minutes

INTRODUCING THE *LIFELINES* PROGRAM TO STUDENTS

The purpose of part 1 is to introduce the *Lifelines* program and to establish a safe atmosphere for discussion. You will be asking students about their experiences related to either hearing about suicide or actually knowing someone who has completed suicide. This discussion helps students connect the classroom information to their own lives.

If this is not your regular class, or if you are co-teaching it with someone new to the class, make introductions. Include some reference to your experience in counseling teens. Talking about your experiences working with teens will engage students more effectively than a recitation of your professional or academic credentials.

1. Ask the class to look at the clock.

2. Explain to the students: **By this time tomorrow, twelve young people in this country between the ages of fifteen and twenty-four will have killed themselves. That means a young person dies by suicide about every two hours. Many more young people attempt suicide every day. Our next four classes will help us better understand what suicide is all about; why someone, especially a teenager, might think about suicide; and how all of us might do something to help.**

3. Acknowledge that the subject of suicide is sometimes difficult to talk about because it involves extremely personal feelings that are often scary and confusing. Briefly discuss each of the ground rules listed on the poster you created.

4. Ask the class to raise their hands in response to the following three questions (acknowledge responses to each question before you move on to the next one):

   • **How many of you have heard about someone in our school or community who has made a suicide attempt?**

   • **How many of you have heard about someone from our town, neighborhood, or school who has died by suicide?** (Usually about 70 to 80 percent of the class will raise their hands.)

   • **Now, how many of you know someone personally who has made a suicide attempt or died by suicide?** Comment on percentage of class who respond affirmatively.

Occasionally a student may want to share his or her personal experience with a suicidal friend or relative. Clearly, once the student speaks up, the comments can't be ignored. It is best to acknowledge the experience or feelings briefly and to relate them to your points in the lesson. Balancing acknowledgment with the need to avoid too much self-disclosure is a difficult judgment call; however, such comments usually contribute positively to the classroom discussion.

5. Explain: **As you can see from your responses, most of you have heard of or personally know someone who has been suicidal. Let me ask another question: If a teen is troubled and thinking about suicide, who do you think will be the first person who knows?** (It is unusual to get an answer other than a friend.) **That is right. You are. Peers and friends are often the first to know if another teen is troubled. That's why the information we are going to be covering in the next few classes is so important. More than anyone else, you may be in a position to help someone who may be thinking about suicide.**

   In this unit we will be discussing how to help a troubled friend. We'll also be talking about how you feel about asking for help for yourself and the resources for help that exist in our school and in the community.

   Suicide prevention is everyone's business and you all play an important part in our school's effort to prevent suicide and other forms of violence. Learning how to prevent suicide makes our school a healthier and safer place. Everyone in the school—including teachers, administrators, school board members, bus drivers, kitchen staff, and custodial staff—has been educated about suicide prevention. Your parents and guardians have also been provided with information. Now these next few sessions will prepare you for your critical role in the prevention process.

WHAT WOULD YOU DO?

The purpose of part 2 is to help students recognize their personal reactions to suicide and to introduce the idea of not keeping secrets about suicidal information. The situation that students are asked to discuss presents the request from a friend to keep a suicidal confidence. It reflects a common challenge in adolescence of maintaining peer allegiances, even in matters of life and death.

Be sure to thoroughly discuss student responses to each question. Sessions 2, 3, and 4 will build on what you cover in this discussion.

 S1-1

1. Pass out the handout What Would You Do? and choose a student to read the situation aloud.

2. Explain: **Please answer the questions about the situation. You will not have to hand in what you write, so feel free to be honest about your thoughts and feelings. You have 5 minutes to think and write and then we will discuss your responses.**

3. When the students have completed their answers, discuss them one at a time. During the discussion, write student responses to the questions on the board and then go back and address each response separately. Leave answers to all questions on the board without erasing so you can refer back to them. The most common (and relevant) responses are listed on the following pages. If your students miss important points, feel free to add them. Preface these remarks with something like: "Other students who have taken these classes have also said . . ."

4. Ask: **How did you respond to the first question, How do you feel when you hear him say this?**

   Possible answers include:

   - Concerned
   - Scared
   - Angry
   - Worried
   - Upset
   - Nothing—he always says things like that to get attention
   - It's not really any of my business
   - Confused
   - Like "Oh, here we go again!"

a. Explain: **So what you are saying is that you might have a lot of different feelings, most of which don't make you feel very good. There are some of you who don't even feel anything, because sometimes we all have friends we don't take too seriously, or we may have friends who threaten things like suicide so often we simply tune them out. And sometimes we may even ignore what someone is saying because we don't know what to say or do.**

5. Ask about the second question: **What do you decide to do or say?**

Possible answers include:

- Nothing, I decide to keep his secret
- Tell another mutual friend
- Tell my parent(s)
- Tell his teacher or my teacher
- Try to talk my friend out of it
- Tell him I can't keep his secret
- Ask him what's upsetting him so much
- Tell him it would be a dumb thing to do
- I don't know what to do

6. **The first response we'll look at is the decision to tell some other person, such as another friend or an adult (parent, teacher, or counselor). Why do you think someone might decide to try this?**

Possible answers include:

- To share the responsibility
- Because you need help figuring out what to do
- Because you're scared
- Because you don't know what else to do

a. **How do you pick the person you decide to tell?**

Possible answers include:

- This adult knows your friend and is in a good position to understand
- You have talked to this person about other things in the past
- You have seen how this teacher/person talks to other kids and he/she seems okay

- You tell this particular friend everything, so this is no exception

- Your parents are helpful in situations like this

- Your friend's parents seem okay to you and you think they ought to know

b. **No matter whom you pick, telling someone else helps both you *and* your friend. You can get the advice and opinion of somebody you trust and don't have to feel like your friend's life is in your hands. And your friend gets the benefit of another person's help. One of the best people to tell is an adult in your school whom you know will listen to you and take you seriously. All the adults in our school have been trained to know what to do in a situation like this. It's important to help your friend get some adult help.**

7. **Now let's look at the suggestion of trying to talk your friend out of it. Why would someone try to do this?**

Possible answers include:

- You can do it right away and not have to wait to find someone to talk to

- Since your friend trusts you, he may listen to you and take your advice

- It keeps it between you and your friend—you don't tell the secret

- Since you know your friend so well, your advice would probably be on target

- You've felt that way yourself, so you understand

a. **This suggestion may let you act quickly and keep your friend's confidence. This one, in fact, may be good to try along with the first idea of talking to someone else. Letting your friend know you care about him and that his life is important to you, even if it isn't important to him right now, may be helpful.**

8. **Let's look at the option of asking your friend what is upsetting him. Why would you do this?**

Possible answers include:

- You may be able to help

- You may have experienced a similar problem

a. While these things may be true, suppose your friend tells you about a terrible problem: about physical or sexual abuse, for example, or about an alcoholic parent? You would probably be surprised or shocked to hear something like that and your reaction might convince your friend that things are hopeless. Remember, lots of problems kids can have can be very complicated. Knowing that your friend is considering suicide, without even asking the reasons why, is enough of a problem. Your friend may really need a professional to help him figure out what to do. If you ask too many questions and get in over your head, both your friend *and* you may need some help.

9. **Another suggestion was to do nothing. Why might someone choose this?**

   Possible answers include:

   - Your friend asked you to keep a secret and it is important to be trustworthy
   - You would want someone to keep your secret if you asked them
   - Your friend is always saying things to get attention and if you did something every time he threatened, you'd look like a fool

   a. While all of these reasons may be true, how do you think you'd feel if he were really serious about taking his life? I think most of us would agree that it is better to have an angry friend who is alive than a friend who is dead.

   b. I hear some of you saying that keeping a secret is important. This is true. But are all secrets the same? Keeping a secret about something that may make the difference between life and death seems to be a special category. Not keeping a secret about suicide is not disloyal or untrustworthy. You break this secret because you are loyal to your friend. You care about his life. Your friend may also be angry with you, but after the crisis has passed, the anger will most likely pass, too. Even if it doesn't, it's a lot easier to live with someone being angry at you than feeling guilty about a friend who is dead or seriously injured because you did nothing to help.

10. **If your friend did share with you that he was feeling suicidal, and you told him that it was a really dumb idea or a stupid thing to do, how do you think that might make him feel?**

    Possible answers include:

    - More isolated and alone than ever
    - Like you don't really understand

- That you aren't listening or you don't care

- Maybe he'd think that nobody cares

a. **This points out to us that there are some things it is better not to do or say to someone feeling suicidal. While these comments won't cause a suicide because each of us is really responsible for our own lives, they may make a person feel even worse. Think for a second of how you'd feel if someone said to you:**

- **"Don't talk like that—it is a stupid idea."**

- **"You wouldn't kill yourself over THAT would you? That's crazy!"**

11. **The last point that I want to make is one of the most important ones** (write on the board as you say it): **One of the most dangerous things you can do is promise to keep suicidal thoughts or behavior a secret.**

It is common for suicidal people to ask that you promise not to tell anyone about their thoughts or plans. They tell you that you are their most trusted friend, the *only* one who can help. This is a very dangerous situation. If your friend had a broken arm, you would get help from someone who knows how to fix broken arms, like a doctor. You wouldn't try to fix it yourself because you couldn't. The same is true for suicide. The most grown-up thing you can do for your friend is to get help. People who care about other people help them find help. It's a brave and courageous thing to do.

PART 3
15 minutes

INFORMATION ABOUT SUICIDE

The purpose of part 3 is to present current and accurate information about youth suicide. Because the topic of suicide is often colored by misinformation and personal attitudes that pose as facts, it's important to provide students with correct information. This section builds on the educational saying, "A problem well-defined is a problem half-solved."

Students will complete a short quiz on basic information about suicide. Over the years, students' *knowledge* about suicide has increased, so this component of the curriculum has been de-emphasized. This section is also given limited time because it is very important to address *attitudes and behaviors* as well as knowledge.

Nine specific questions are included, but you may wish to emphasize a different fact about suicide in your class. You may also wish to present new information about youth suicide as it becomes available. For these reasons, items may be substituted for current quiz items except for items 1, 2, 7, 8, 9.

1. Explain: **I'm going to hand out a quiz that is different from the usual type of quiz we take in class. You don't have to turn this quiz in and you don't have to know the right answers because I'm going to give them to you. This is just to give you an idea of what you already know about teen suicide and provide us with some questions for discussion.**

 S1-2

2. Hand out the questionnaire and allow a couple of minutes for students to complete it.

3. Explain: **I'm going to ask how many of you responded "true" and how many of you responded "false" to each question. Then I'll give you the correct answer and the facts on which it is based.**

4. Read each question aloud (or ask students to do so) and review the reasons for the correct answer.

   1. *People who talk about suicide do not actually kill themselves. False.*

      Read aloud or summarize the following:

      Most people who die by suicide talk with at least one other person about their suicidal feelings or plans before they finally decide to act on them. It is important to take these communications seriously even if the person says she or he did not really mean it.

   2. *Suicide happens without warning signs. False.*

      Read aloud or summarize the following:

      Most people give us clues that they are thinking about taking their lives. The warning signs include things like making direct statements about dying, losing interest in everything they used to care about before, feeling really miserable and unhappy, and showing changes in attitudes or behaviors like not taking care of themselves, quitting teams, or being tired all the time. Usually a person shows more than one sign. There are, however, a small percentage of people who die by suicide without leaving clues.

   3. *Suicide occurs equally as often among rich, middle class, and poor people. True.*

      Read aloud or summarize the following:

      Suicidal behavior occurs in people of all income levels. In fact, people of all ages, races, faiths, cultures, and walks of life die by suicide. Both "popular" people who seem to have everything going for them and people who are

"down and out" die by suicide. Suicidal teens come from all kinds of families. This is why we have to pay serious attention to all suicidal talk and behavior.

4. *Males die by suicide more often than females. True.*

Read aloud or summarize the following:

Men do die by suicide more than females, but females make more attempts than men do. It isn't that women aren't as serious about dying as men are, it's just that they choose methods that are less lethal and that give them time to change their minds. It's so important to understand that most people *will* change their minds and want to be rescued.

This question does present us with another issue, and that's how we talk about suicide. The words we use are very important. When we say someone was "successful at suicide" that's a bit of a contradiction. It's like saying you're good at doing something that hurts yourself. And people whose lives have been touched by suicide often feel that using the term "successful" is insensitive. Even talking about "committing suicide" can seem a bit insensitive. When we talk about "committing" something in our society, we are usually talking about committing a crime. And suicide isn't a crime. It's just a very, very bad decision made by someone who isn't thinking clearly. Instead, using the words "completed suicide" or "died by suicide" is appropriate, sensitive, and correct.

5. *Once a person is suicidal, he or she is suicidal forever. False.*

Read aloud or summarize the following:

People can be helped, often with the aid of professional counseling from someone like a psychologist or social worker, to see other, less destructive solutions to their problems. If they do get help, the vast majority of people who make suicidal attempts *do not* go on to kill themselves.

6. *If a person feels better after a suicide attempt, it means he or she will probably not try to do it again. False.*

Read aloud or summarize the following:

If the attempt brings a lot of temporary attention and support or even popularity, the person may feel better for a while. But unless there are changes in the person's life or the person gets help in managing problems with better coping skills, he or she may be at risk for another attempt. In addition, the person may have to deal with all the disapproving things people say about someone who has made a suicide attempt. This adds something else that is negative to the problems the person had in the first place and can also increase his or her risk for another suicide attempt. That's why it's so important for someone who has attempted suicide or is even thinking about it to get good, professional help.

7. *Suicidal people really want to die. False.*

   Read aloud or summarize the following:

   Sometimes this is true, but usually suicidal people simply want to escape the terrible way they are feeling, not end their lives. Many people who attempt suicide call on someone to help them immediately after they have made their attempt. Or, they may tell someone about their plan to make an attempt and try to swear the person to secrecy. This is why suicide intervention is so important. People who attempt suicide are emotionally mixed-up at the time and not thinking very calmly and clearly. Later, most are grateful that someone saved them.

8. *Talking about suicide or asking someone about suicide may put the idea in the person's head and cause suicide. False.*

   Read aloud or summarize the following:

   Actually, the opposite is often true. Asking directly about suicidal ideas or intentions can help people who feel like there's no one they can talk to about how terrible they are feeling. In fact, talking out feelings can help prevent the person from acting on them. Think about a time in your life when you were really upset about something and felt like you had to keep it to yourself; that no one would really understand. If you were able to share those worries with someone else, my guess is that you probably felt a lot better.

9. *People who threaten to kill themselves are just seeking attention. False.*

   Read aloud or summarize the following:

   We must *not* dismiss a suicide threat or attempt as simply being an attention-getting device. If people are so desperate for attention that the only way they can think of getting it is to threaten to kill themselves, then they really *do* need attention. But they need attention from someone who can truly help them to not feel this way. All talk, threats, and attempts must be taken seriously and shared with an adult who is in a position to help.

PART 4
2 minutes

WRAP-UP

1. Explain: **We've learned today that youth suicide is a big problem that has touched many of your lives. We've talked about the fact that you may be one of the first people to know if a friend is having problems or thinking about suicide.**

2. Ask: **What did we say was one of the most important ways that you could help a friend who might be thinking about suicide?** (Respond to raised hands and continue to ask for input until you get the answer "talk to an adult." Validate all answers but reinforce the importance of talking with an adult.)

3. Conclude: **In our next class, we're going to learn about warning signs for suicide and begin to talk about specific ways for helping friends who may be in need.**

How Do I Help a Friend?

....

DESCRIPTION

Through discussion guided by a handout and DVD scenarios, students will begin to explore specific intervention steps to use when responding to suicidal friends. An additional handout will help them identify suicide warning signs.

LEARNER OUTCOMES

By the end of the session, students will be able to

- recognize specific warning signs of suicide in themselves and others
- organize warning signs around the FACTS sheet
- name three basic suicide intervention steps
- identify the words to use to ask about suicide

MATERIALS NEEDED

- Board or flipchart and markers
- DVD player and monitor
- *A Teen's Guide to Suicide Prevention* video from the *Lifelines* DVD

- Handouts from CD-ROM:
  - Warning Signs of Suicide/FACTS 📄 **S2-1**
  - *A Teen's Guide to Suicide Prevention* Discussion Guidelines 📄 **S2-2**
  - Helpful Steps to Prevent Suicide 📄 **S2-3**

PREPARATION NEEDED

- Read the session outline.
- Print and photocopy handouts, one per student.
- Set up the DVD player and monitor.
- Post the ground rules from session 1, if they aren't still up.

Session 2 Outline

PART 1
5 minutes

This session moves along rather quickly. Keep to the time limits in each part to ensure enough time to view the video, which is the main part of this session and reinforces the learning of the other parts.

IDENTIFYING WARNING SIGNS OF SUICIDE

The purpose of part 1 is to identify the most common warning signs of youth suicide. With this awareness, students should be better able to recognize signs of distress in a friend or a peer.

There are a number of lists of suicide warning signs and, unfortunately, there is no "official" list that is agreed on by all experts. There is no research to-date that shows that a particular set of risk factors or warning signs can accurately predict the likelihood of imminent danger of suicide for a specific individual. Even experts do not always agree when asked to assess the degree of suicide risk for given cases. For now, it may be best to stick to the list in the handout, which includes some of the most commonly acknowledged warning signs, and avoid including other signs; otherwise, the list becomes useless. (To stay apprised of the most current research on risk factors and warning signs, visit www.suicidology.org, the Web site of the American Association of Suicidology.)

1. Explain: **Most teens give some kind of warning signs or clues that they are experiencing problems and may be considering suicide. Even though the signs do not necessarily mean that a person is suicidal, it is important to know what some of the warning signs of suicide are so that you can recognize them and intervene appropriately.**

2. Explain: **The word "FACTS" is one way to organize different kinds of warning signs of suicidal behavior.** Write on the board:

> **F—Feelings**
> **A—Actions**
> **C—Changes**
> **T—Threats**
> **S—Situations**

3. Distribute the Warning Signs of Suicide/FACTS handout.

4. Review the handout. Read each category. If needed, you can add short examples to clarify student questions, but the list tends to be self-explanatory.

5. Explain: **Of course, aside from obvious threats or attempts, none of these signs is a definite indication that a person is going to die by suicide. Many people are depressed and never end their lives. Many others experience losses or show changes in behavior with no indication of suicide. However, if a number of these signs occur, they may be important clues. Since people who attempt suicide are in emotional trouble, it is important to risk the possibility of overreacting rather than underreacting, and tell an adult if you see any of the things on this list and are concerned about a friend.**

> **It's also important to recognize that there are two things that dramatically increase the danger of suicide.**
>
> - **One is alcohol and/or drug use. This tends to impair a person's judgment, which means they do not make good decisions. It also increases the things that are done without thinking, which is called "impulsivity."**
>
> - **The second thing that dramatically increases suicide risk is access to a gun. Guns are the number one way that teens kill themselves.**
>
> **If you have a friend who is drinking or using drugs, or who has a gun, stay with the person and get help immediately.**

PART 2
19 minutes

DVD SCENARIOS: *A TEEN'S GUIDE TO SUICIDE PREVENTION*

The purpose of part 2 is to model appropriate student responses to a troubled peer. To engage students in the content, four role-played scenarios are used to demonstrate the different ways teens involve adults in helping at-risk friends.

1. Explain: **This video was created to demonstrate what to do and what *not* to do if a peer is talking about suicide or showing warning signs. It reviews some of the information about suicide that we talked about in our first session and some of the warning signs we just reviewed with the word "FACTS." You're going to see four role-plays that demonstrate friends helping friends. All four role-plays discuss involving an adult. I'm going to pass out a handout that lists several things I'd like you to pay attention to. First, I'd like you to identify the warning signs you see in each scenario. Then I'd like you to observe who the adults are that the friends turn to for help and how they do that.**

S2-2

2. Distribute the *A Teen's Guide to Suicide Prevention* Discussion Guidelines handout.

3. Play *A Teen's Guide to Suicide Prevention* from the *Lifelines* DVD.

PART 3
10 minutes

A TEEN'S GUIDE TO SUICIDE PREVENTION DISCUSSION

The purpose of part 3 is twofold: to reinforce awareness of suicide warning signs, and to identify the differences and similarities in the ways in which adults can be involved in the helping process.

Because texting is one of the main ways teens communicate, it is essential to discuss this role-play from the video.

1. Using students' answers to the *A Teen's Guide to Suicide Prevention* Discussion Guidelines handout, ask the following discussion questions. (Suggested responses are provided for your reference. If students do not make these key points, add them yourself.)

   a. **What are some of the key warning signs or "FACTS" you observed that made the kids in the video think that their friends might be at risk for suicide?**

      • A sudden or significant change in behavior or attitude

      • Having made a suicide attempt in the past

      • Making a suicide threat

      • Having a current suicide plan (Note: Make the point that if the person also has the means to carry out the plan, the risk is high and immediate.)

      • Alcohol and/or drug use

b. **All four role-plays show the young people involving an adult. Whom did they involve and how?**

- Emphasize that if the risk is high and immediate, the nearest adult should be involved. This was illustrated in the scene with Isaac and Blake. The minute Blake shared that he knew the location of his father's gun, Isaac suggested they talk to his older brother.

- In the remaining three scenes, the teens were encouraged to choose a particular adult that they would be willing to talk to, and they were given firm support by their friends for making that effort.

- In the role-play with Teresa and Susie, Teresa suggested finding a different adult to talk to if the first person they went to wasn't helpful.

c. **In the video, the hosts spoke about "remembering your limits." How would you know if you were in over your head when trying to help a friend?**

Possible responses include:

- I'd be scared about something they said

- I wouldn't know how to respond to them

- They'd talk about having already tried to kill themselves

- They would say things I wouldn't believe; like they were okay when I'd know they weren't

- The minute they said the word "suicide," I'd know I needed to get some help

2. Summarize: **In these video scenes, you saw teens interacting with friends who were showing warning signs of suicide risk. These teens demonstrated for us how to acknowledge concern about risk and how to suggest to their friends that they go to a trusted adult for additional help.**

PART 4
10 minutes

HELPFUL STEPS TO PREVENT SUICIDE

The purpose of part 4 is to provide students with three basic intervention steps that they can use to respond to a possibly suicidal person:[2]

- Show you care

- Ask about suicide

- Get help

To increase students' comfort level in their ability to intervene, encourage them to find "their own words" for carrying out these three steps.

1. Ask students to pair up with a partner. Depending on the composition of your class, this pairing may be based on either student self-selection or your assignment.

S2-3

2. Distribute the Helpful Steps to Prevent Suicide handout.

3. Explain: **There are three steps we need to take when we are trying to help a friend who might be thinking about suicide. You saw them demonstrated in the scenarios we just watched on the DVD, and now you're going to get a chance to use your own words to describe how you would intervene. The three steps are listed on your handout.** Write these steps on the board as you discuss them, and leave them on the board for the remainder of the session:

   - **finding the words to show you care about your friend**

   - **asking about suicide**

   - **convincing your friend to ask for help**

   a. **Your assignment is to**

      - **think about and write one or two phrases that you would use to show caring**

      - **write two other ways to ask about suicide**

      - **write two things you might say to convince a friend to get help**

   b. **You and your partner will have a few minutes to do this assignment, and then we're going to talk about it together as a class.** Give students about 5 minutes to record their responses on the handout.

4. To reinforce and review the steps of a basic suicide intervention, ask partners to share their ideas with the entire group. Write responses under each heading on the board. Keep this discussion moving very quickly. This is a form of brainstorming so all answers, unless mean-spirited, are acceptable.

   a. Say: **I'd like to hear the words you would use to show you care.** Before moving on, listen to several statements students might have come up with, such as:

      - You don't seem to be yourself. I'm worried about you.

- I'm concerned. You have never been this "down" before.

- What is going on? What's making you feel so out of control?

b. Then ask: **How would you ask about suicide?** Ask for several examples, such as:

- Are you talking about suicide?

- Are you thinking about killing yourself?

- Do you mean you want to end your life?

c. **And finally, what words would you use to convince a friend to get help?**

- You are not alone. Let me help you get help.

- This is really serious. I want to help you right now. Who do you feel comfortable talking to? How about we go talk to the coach?

- I know a crisis number we can call to talk this over.

PART 5
1 minute

WRAP-UP

1. Explain: **Today we've discussed how we move from knowledge about suicide and its warning signs to action. One of the most important things we learned is that it's *important* to ask directly about suicide if you're concerned about a friend.**

   Another important thing we saw practiced in the DVD was how to convince a friend to go to an adult for help.

2. Conclude: **I'd like you to continue to think about what we learned, especially about these three intervention steps, and the other things you might say to show you care, to ask about suicide, and to convince a friend to go for help. We'll learn more about these in our next class.**

Where Can I Go to Get Help?

....

DESCRIPTION

Students will view the dramatization of a real-life suicide intervention undertaken by three students in Maine, using the skills they learned in the *Lifelines* curriculum. Through a classroom activity, students will identify the qualities of helpful people. Discussion will also review in-school and community resources.

LEARNER OUTCOMES

By the end of the session, students will be able to

- discuss more fully how to implement the steps of a successful peer intervention

- define traits of helpful people

- identify school resources and procedures for responding to suicidal students

MATERIALS NEEDED

- *One Life Saved: The Story of a Suicide Intervention* video from the *Lifelines* DVD

- DVD player and monitor

- Handouts from CD-ROM:

  - Warning Signs of Suicide/FACTS from session 2 ⌷ **S2-1**

109

• *One Life Saved* Discussion Questions 🗐 **S3-1**

• The Qualities of Helpful People 🗐 **S3-2**

- (Optional) Handout on school procedure for responding to suicidal students (see part 3)

- Board or flipchart and markers

- Chart paper with questions for discussion

- Masking tape

- Homework assignments for selected students (role-play scripts from session 4)

PREPARATION NEEDED

- Read the session outline.

- Select discussion questions for The Qualities of Helpful People activity (see part 2). You will be dividing the class into groups of three or four and assigning each group two or three of these questions to answer. Using the chart paper, write one question at the top of each sheet of paper, making sure to have two or three questions/sheets of paper per group. You will be distributing these to the groups to record their answers. Cut strips of masking tape so completed answer sheets can be posted in front of the room to facilitate discussion.

- Print and photocopy handouts, one per student.

- Set up DVD player and monitor.

- Post the ground rules from session 1, if they aren't still up.

🗐 **S4-1**

- Read the role-plays for session 4 (found on the CD-ROM) and select two or three for class discussion. Print out the role-plays you selected and make three copies of each role-play. Feel free to adjust the dialogue of the role-plays to reflect your particular student population. Each role-play will require two actors and a moderator. Review the class roster and choose three students for each role-play. These students should be reliable and outgoing and agree not to discuss the role-plays with other classmates prior to class. They should also be willing to practice reading the parts out loud to get comfortable with their lines. You can enlist the participation of these students and hand out the scripts at the beginning or end of this session.

Session 3 Outline

PART 1
15 minutes

ONE LIFE SAVED AND DISCUSSION QUESTIONS

The purpose of part 1 is to illustrate for students how to apply the three steps of the peer intervention they learned in session 2 (show you care, ask about suicide, and get help). The real-life experience of students from Maine is dramatically described in the video and provides a concrete example of how to implement the steps. *Lifelines* author Maureen Underwood also discusses the important role of the counselor in this situation. An important reason for including this particular video is that it focuses on the students who performed the intervention and not on the person who was feeling suicidal.

1. Explain to the students: **This video, titled *One Life Saved,* tells the true story of a suicide intervention that took place several years ago after the completion of the *Lifelines* student lessons in a Maine school. It illustrates how three young men recognized the warning signs of suicide in a friend and what they did to help him.**

 S2-1, S3-1

2. Distribute the Warning Signs of Suicide/FACTS handout and *One Life Saved* Discussion Questions. Explain: **Here's a copy of the handout we talked about in the last session. As you watch this video, look at the FACTS handout. Listen carefully for the FACTS that the boys noticed in their friend: the feelings; the actions or events that led to the feelings; the changes in the way he acted; the threats that he made; and the situations you think contributed to his feelings. Use the *One Life Saved* Discussion Questions to help organize what you notice. We'll talk about what you observed after we watch this short film.**

In *One Life Saved,* the writing on the wall says:

"It seems that every day I want to leave more and more until the day I have to leave."

—AB

3. Play *One Life Saved* from the *Lifelines* DVD.

4. Ask: **After hearing TJ's story, how do you think he might have been feeling, the "F" on the FACTS sheet?**

   Possible answers include:

   - Sad
   - Upset about his dad's death
   - Desperate
   - Confused
   - He said he hated life
   - Like no one liked him

5. **What "A" actions or events was TJ experiencing that were very stressful for him?**

Possible answers include:

- Teasing from others about his athletic ability and girls
- His mother's sadness about his dad's death

a. Explain: **When a parent dies, like TJ's dad, everyone in the family is affected. And although everyone in the family experiences the same loss, each family member will react to it in a very personal way. Because of these different reactions, family members can often feel very alone and isolated, even from each other. His dad's death sounds like it's the "S" situation that really pushed TJ over the edge, doesn't it?**

The support of peers and friends can really help someone like TJ in a difficult situation like this. And it's important to recognize that even though these three boys used to tease TJ, they can still be helpful, caring friends.

6. **What changes, the "C" in FACTS, did his friends observe?**

Possible answers include:

- He was no longer "happy-go-lucky"
- Saying things like "Nobody would care if . . ."

a. Explain: **The boys (Gabe, Sean, and Sam) may not have realized that the behavior changes and comments they noticed were actually warning signs of suicide if they had not learned about them in class. Research shows that many people who are thinking about suicide often give some warning signs, especially in the week or two before an attempt.**

7. **What "T" threats did the boys hear TJ mention?**

Possible answers include:

- "Everybody would be better off without me"
- "I'm gonna kill myself"
- A plan to use his "very high roof" as a way to kill himself

a. Explain: **What the boys heard was not just a threat from TJ but an actual plan. While the threat itself was serious, the fact that TJ had a plan made the situation even more dangerous. And what the boys did was the absolutely correct thing to do: they went to talk to a trusted adult.**

8. What "S" situation contributed to TJ's feelings?

Answer:

- his dad's death

9. Now let's talk about some of the positive things TJ had going for him. What were they?

Possible answers include:

- Friends and adults who knew what to do
- The ability to communicate his feelings
- A caring parent very willing to help

a. Explain: **These positive things are called "protective factors" because they help protect us in difficult situations. They're kind of like the bumper that protects the body of the car when it gets bumped in an accident. Protective factors for kids can be your friends, your involvement in school activities or your church, or having a caring adult in your life that you trust.**

10. So Gabe, Sean, and Sam were "protective factors" for TJ. What did they do to try to help him?

Possible answers include:

- Showed they cared (listened, noticed different behaviors)
- Asked about suicide (twice!)
- Got help from an adult they trusted
- Stayed with TJ until the guidance counselor got there

a. Explain: **These three steps—show you care, ask about what's concerning you, and go to an adult you trust for help—are simple and easy to remember.**

11. What was TJ's immediate response to his friends' trying to help him?

Possible answers include:

- He accused the boys of overreacting
- Told them that they weren't his friends anymore

a. Explain: **TJ's reaction isn't so unusual. Even if friends have told you upsetting things, they might initially get angry when you suggest they need some help from an adult. Usually their anger passes once the crisis is over and they've gotten**

Caution: Questions may surface about TJ and the outcome of the intervention. Remind the class that the purpose of the DVD is to highlight the three boys and the steps they took to intervene with a friend. They were in no way responsible for the final outcome. If TJ had ultimately decided to take his life, the boys would not be responsible for his decision. However, TJ did receive both immediate crisis intervention and ongoing help. He and his family worked through their grief over the death of his father. TJ graduated from high school in June 2007.

help. Even if the anger doesn't go away, it is easier to live with a friend's anger than with your own guilt over a friend who is dead or seriously injured. We must not keep suicide a secret. (And to give you the inside story on this real-life situation, TJ's anger lasted less than a week and all of the boys remain friends.)

12. **How did Gabe, Sean, and Sam feel about what they did?**

Possible answers include:

- Really proud

- Happy they could help a friend

a. Explain: **This story shows us that friends who pay attention and know what to do can really make a lifesaving difference. These boys are teaching us that suicide can be prevented and that any one of us can make a difference.**

<table>
<tr><td>**PART 2**
25 minutes</td></tr>
</table>

THE QUALITIES OF HELPFUL PEOPLE

The purpose of part 2 is to help students define the qualities in the people they find helpful. Because the perception of helpfulness is so individual, this topic creates the opportunity for interesting classroom discussion. As you discuss this topic, be sure to make the following points:

- Everyone needs help at some point in his or her life.

- Everyone finds himself or herself in the position of being able to help someone else at some point in his or her life.

- Our school system has planned how adults can and will be helpful in the event of suicide-related behavior.

1. Explain: **In the story about TJ, we saw that when his friends realized they couldn't handle the situation, they went to their guidance counselor for help. I'd like to think that all kids have an adult like that guidance counselor to talk to. But I know that sometimes kids are reluctant to turn to adults for help.**

2. Ask: **What are some reasons why teens might be reluctant to go to adults for help?**

Common answers include:

- Students don't know what the adult will do or what will happen if they tell an adult.

- The adult may not know what to do.

- Adults don't understand kids the way friends do.

- The adult won't take them seriously or will overreact.

- The adult will cause even more trouble (parents will be angry when called).

- Their friends will be mad at them if they tell an adult.

- Kids don't want to "rock the boat" or disappoint parents or admit to needing help.

3. Summarize: **There may be a lot of reasons why adults may not seem approachable when you need help. But I'm sure there are also many reasons to talk to an adult when you have a problem. That's what we're going to explore next.**

4. Divide the class into groups of three or four. Use your knowledge of the students to create functional work groups. Distribute The Qualities of Helpful People handout.

 S3-2

5. Explain: **Each small group will be given two or three questions to answer about the qualities of helpful people. Your questions are written on large sheets of paper. I'll give each group a marker so you can write your answers on the paper to share with the rest of the class. You will have about 5 minutes to complete the assignment. Use the handout to help answer the questions.**

6. Choose your questions from the list below and on the top of page 116. These questions lend themselves to small group work. They are designed to empower students to seek help from adults and/or be helpful to others. Pick questions that will work best for your groups or write your own. When the groups have finished answering their questions, tell them to post their responses in the front of the room to facilitate discussion.

- If you were on a committee to hire a new counselor at our school whose only responsibility would be to help students, what characteristics would you look for in this person?

- In your experience, what qualities make a person trustworthy?

- In your experience, what qualities make a person helpful?

- If you were looking for help, how would you check out a person to find out whether or not he or she would be a good person to approach?

- What can you do personally to make it more likely that people will turn to you for help?

Lifelines

. . . .

116

- What makes it hard to get help from adults in our school?
- What do you suggest should be done to improve helpful resources for students?

PART 3
3 minutes

INFORM STUDENTS OF YOUR SCHOOL'S PREPAREDNESS TO HELP

The purpose of part 3 is to assure your students that the adults in the school have received training so that they will know how to respond to situations involving suicidal behavior. Students are reminded that not every member of the staff may demonstrate the qualities they personally find helpful; so, if students are not satisfied with the response from the first adult, they should immediately find another trusted adult. Also reviewed is the school's response when a potentially suicidal student is identified.

1. Explain: **The question of whom students can go to to get help is so crucial that everyone in the school has been trained to know what to do if they are approached by a student with a concern about suicide. It's also important to remember what we just learned in our activity today about the different qualities of helpful people; how what one person finds helpful may be very unhelpful to someone else. So, if you go to a teacher to ask for help and the response isn't something that really helps you, go find another teacher or staff member to talk to.**

2. Next, students should be told exactly what the school's procedure is when a potentially suicidal student is identified. This can be summarized in a handout. For example:

   When a potentially suicidal student has been called to the attention of any adult in the school, that adult will contact one of the school personnel who has been trained and designated to respond to this kind of situation. In our school those people are (name the individuals). One of these individuals will talk privately with the student to find out what is bothering him or her. If the adult is concerned about this person being at risk for suicide, the parents/guardians will be contacted and the student will be referred for help. You may contact any adult in the school on your own if you are worried about someone else, and, if you wish, your name will not be revealed.

3. Explain: **Sometimes students worry that their parents will be angry or upset with them if the school contacts them. And while there's no guarantee that this won't happen, remember that the resource person is there to explain to parents the reasons for the school's concerns and how important it is for the student to get help.**

    Students may also worry about the reactions of a friend, but the video we saw today reminds us that it's a lot better to have an angry friend than a dead friend.

<table>
<tr><td>

PART 4

2 minutes
</td><td>

WRAP-UP

1. Explain: **This class gave us a dramatic picture of how helpful friends can be to each other when one of them is thinking about suicide. We could also see how to use some of the suggestions for helping that we've been learning about in the** *Lifelines* **program.**

2. Ask: **What were some of the qualities you identified as important in helpful people?** Respond to raised hands to get a sampling of responses.

3. Conclude: **In our next class, you'll see how you can put into practice what you've learned about helping a friend who may be thinking about suicide.**
</td></tr>
</table>

How Can I Use What I've Learned?

DESCRIPTION

Session 4 uses scripted role-plays to practice intervening in suicidal behavior. A help-seeking pledge further commits students to taking action for themselves and others, and also clarifies the limits of their responsibility. A wallet card serves as a review and a resource.

LEARNER OUTCOMES

By the end of the session, students will be able to

- demonstrate ability to help a troubled friend through scripted role-plays
- demonstrate willingness to help self or a troubled friend by signing a help-seeking pledge
- identify the wallet card as a resource

MATERIALS NEEDED

- Board or flipchart and markers
- Handouts from CD-ROM:
    - Role-Play Scenarios (for actors and moderators) 📇 S4-1
    - Role-Play Discussion 📇 S4-2
    - Warning Signs of Suicide/FACTS, from session 2 📇 S2-1

119

- Help-Seeking Pledge 📄 **S4-3**
- *Lifelines* Wallet Card 📄 **S4-4**

PREPARATION NEEDED

- Prior to class, check in with the students you selected to participate in the role-plays to make sure they are prepared. Make extra copies of the role-plays in case they have forgotten to bring the copies you gave them at the last class session.

- Review the instructions for the role-plays.

- Print and photocopy handouts, one for each student.

- Copy the wallet cards. These cards are designed to be carried by the students at all times. They should therefore be printed on sufficiently strong stock to stand up to use; 8-point white-coated cover stock is recommended. Students won't want to advertise the fact that they are carrying a card with help-seeking information, so use an unobtrusive color. Alternatively you can create your own wallet cards. Use an easy-to-read font and print them on heavy paper stock.

- Post the ground rules from session 1, if they aren't still up.

Session 4 Outline

PART 1
30 minutes

GUIDED PRACTICE THROUGH SCRIPTED ROLE-PLAYS

The purpose of this section is to use role-plays to involve all students as "helpers." Class members have been preselected to present the role-plays while the rest of the class is instructed to concentrate on the student in the "helper's role."

Each role-play has two scenes. The first scene presents the warning signs of suicide and the suicidal person's resistance to help. There is a "break" between scenes with discussion questions provided to give the class time to make comments and suggestions. The second scene demonstrates the "helper" completing a suicide intervention, followed by more questions to the class. The questions can be facilitated by the student moderator and/or the teacher.

When responding to the discussion questions, many students will initially answer in the way they feel is expected of them. For example, they will indicate that they would break their friend's (or relative's) confidence and "tell an adult"

Student Curriculum, Session 4: How Can I Use What I've Learned?

121

even if they honestly remain unconvinced that they would or should, especially if the situation is ambiguous. The break between the two role-play scenes gives the students the opportunity to explore the reasons for and the consequences of different responses.

This session provides the opportunity to emphasize the following:

- Keeping suicidal behavior a secret is a form of assuming responsibility.

- One should never promise to keep suicide a secret.

- One of the best things a friend can do is to recognize his or her limits and get the help needed from trusted adults.

1. Explain: **The object of this lesson is for our class to participate in some situations that present the opportunity to intervene in suicidal behavior. We will use the suicide prevention steps we learned about in sessions 2 and 3.**

2. Ask: **What were those steps?**

    - Show you care

    - Ask about suicide

    - Get help

3. Distribute Role-Play Discussion and Warning Signs of Suicide/FACTS handouts.

 S4-2, S2-1

4. Explain: **Today, some of your classmates have agreed to present some role-plays that were actually written by other students who have participated in the *Lifelines* program. Each role-play has two scenes. In the middle of each role-play, there will be an opportunity to talk about what might be going on. As you watch and listen, use your Role-Play Discussion handout to record the FACTS. Also think about what you would do and say if you were trying to help this friend or relative.**

5. Taking time to set up the role-plays will make it easier to debrief the actors after the role-plays are over. Select a location in front of the class for the stage. Invite the actors in the first role-play to take their places.

6. Explain: **As you know, role-plays are like acting. So we're going to help our actors take their cues by using the technique that's used in filming: starting the role-play by calling out as a group "One—Two—Three—Action!" At the end of the scene, the moderator for that scene will call "Cut" to bring our actors out of their roles.** (These simple techniques help put boundaries on the role-playing and make it easier for the involved students to step out of the action and back

into the regular structure of the class. You will want to encourage that transition as quickly and effectively as possible, especially for the actor playing the suicidal student.)

7. At the end of each role-play, be sure to recognize and reinforce that all three steps were taken:

   - Caring words were expressed.

   - A direct suicide-related question was asked.

   - Help was identified and sought after.

Emphasize that caring alone is not enough when suicidal behavior is being expressed. The second and third steps are essential.

If you would like to learn more about maximizing the effectiveness of this role-playing technique, a helpful resource is *Clinical Applications of Drama Therapy in Child and Adolescent Treatment,* edited by A. M. Weber and C. Haen (New York: Brunner-Routledge, 2005).

8. As soon as the role-play is over, ask the actors to take a deep breath, shake off the character they were playing, and return to their seats for the debriefing. By giving these directions, you begin to help the students disengage from their roles. Use the real names of the students involved and thank them for their participation. Ask the actors if they would like to share anything about what it was like to play their roles.

PART 2
10 minutes

THE HELP-SEEKING PLEDGE

The purpose of part 2 is to invite students to formally commit to the idea of seeking help for themselves or a friend. Created by students in Maine, this simple pledge is designed to encourage the identification of helpful adults.

The pledge can be used at the close of session 3 after discussing the qualities of helpful people or as part of the closing activities in session 4. It can be kept by the students, collected by the teacher, or even signed in duplicate so that one copy can be kept and one copy can be collected.

1. Explain: **In the last part of our class today, we're going to talk about making a help-seeking pledge.**

2. Ask: **Can anyone tell me the meaning of a pledge?** Solicit responses from the class until you get the answer that a pledge is a promise.

3. Explain: **The promise I'm going to ask you to make today is actually a promise to yourself. In these *Lifelines* classes, you have learned to recognize the signs of suicidal behavior and you know how to get help. The promise you are making to yourself is if you see signs of suicidal behavior in yourself or someone else, you**

Student Curriculum, Session 4: How Can I Use What I've Learned?

123

will get help from a trusted adult. This help-seeking pledge was created by students in Maine as a way to formally commit to the idea of seeking help for yourself or for a friend.

S4-3

4. Hand out copies of the Help-Seeking Pledge.

5. Explain: **On this pledge, you'll see that you are asked to identify three people to whom you would turn if you needed help for yourself or someone else. I'd like you to write in the names of three people you trust, and if you have their contact information, add that, too. If not, you can take this pledge home with you and add that information tonight.**

PART 3
5 minutes

WRAP-UP

1. Explain: **We've learned a lot about suicide prevention in these four sessions and it's the kind of information that you will be able to use for the rest of your lives. Although we've had a lot of thoughtful and interesting classroom discussion, there are some key points that are important for you to remember.**

   This information has been printed for you on a small card that you can keep in your wallet or another safe, easily accessible place.

S4-4

2. Hand out wallet cards.

3. Explain: **This small card summarizes all the information we've covered in this** *Lifelines* **unit on suicide prevention. It reminds you about the warning signs we've talked about. And, more importantly, it reinforces the fact that the first thing to do if you're worried about yourself or a friend being suicidal is to tell a trusted adult. It even gives you room to write down the names and phone numbers of the adults you know you can go to if you need help. Program these phone numbers into your cell phone so you have them with you at all times.**

   Remember these three key points:

   • **Show a friend you care.**

   • **Ask about suicide.**

   • **Get help from a trusted adult!**

Notes

....

Introduction to *Lifelines*

1. J. Kalafat and M. Elias, "Adolescents' Experience with and Response to Suicidal Peers," *Suicide and Life-Threatening Behavior* 22 (1992): 315–21; J. Kalafat, M. Elias, and M. A. Gara, "The Relationship of Bystander Intervention Variables to Adolescents' Response to Suicidal Peers," *The Journal of Primary Prevention* 13 (1993): 213, 231–44; J. Kalafat and M. Elias, "An Evaluation of Adolescent Suicide Intervention Classes," *Suicide and Life-Threatening Behavior* 24 (1994): 224–33; J. Kalafat, "The Prevention of Youth Suicide," in *Healthy Children 2010: Enhancing Children's Wellness*, eds. R. P. Weissberg, T. P. Gullota, B. A. Ryan, and G. R. Adams, 175–213 (Thousand Oaks, CA: Sage, 1997); C. R. Lindsay and J. Kalafat, "Adolescents' Views of Preferred Helper Characteristics and Barriers to Seeking Help from School-based Adults," *Journal of Educational and Psychological Consultation* 9 (1998): 171–93; J. Kalafat, "A Systems Approach to Suicide Prevention," in *Suicide Prevention and Intervention: Summary of an Institute of Medicine Workshop*, ed. S. K. Goldsmith, 4–7 (Washington, DC: National Academy Press, 2001).

Introduction to Teen Suicide

1. American Association of Suicidology, 2008 (data gathered in 2005). Check www.suicidology.org for updated statistics.

2. Youth Risk Behavior Survey (Atlanta: Centers for Disease Control and Prevention, 2007).

3. Ernest L. Boyer, *The Basic School: A Community for Learning* (Princeton, NJ: The Carnegie Foundation for the Advancement of Teaching, 1995).

4. P. Hazell and P. Lewin, "An Evaluation of Postvention Following Adolescent Suicide," *Suicide and Life-Threatening Behavior* 23 (1993): 101–109; M. M. Underwood and K. Dunne-Maxim, *Managing Sudden Traumatic Loss in the Schools: New Jersey Adolescent Suicide Prevention Project* (Piscataway, NJ: University Behavioral HealthCare, 1997); S. Poland, "Suicide Intervention," in *Best Practices in School Psychology-II*, eds. A. Thomas and J. Grimes, 259–74 (Washington, DC: National Association of School Psychologists, 1995); J. Kalafat and M. Elias, "An Evaluation of Adolescent Suicide Intervention Classes," *Suicide and Life-Threatening Behavior* 24 (1994): 224–33; V. Vieland, B. Whittle, A. Garland, R. Hicks, and D. Shaffer, "The Impact of Curriculum-based Suicide Prevention Programs for Teenagers: An 18-month Follow-up," *Journal of the American Academy of Child and Adolescent Psychiatry* 30 (1991): 811–15; J. Cliffone, "Suicide Prevention: A Classroom Presentation to Adolescents," *Social Work* 38 (1993): 197–203.

5. See J. Kalafat and M. Elias, "Adolescents' Experience with and Response to Suicidal Peers," *Suicide and Life-Threatening Behavior* 22 (1992): 315–21.

6. See *Youth Suicide Prevention Programs: A Resource Guide* (Atlanta: Centers for Disease Control and Prevention, 1992), 66.

7. See L. Potter, K. E. Powell, and S. P. Kacher, "Suicide Prevention from a Mental Health Perspective," *Suicide and Life-Threatening Behavior* 25 (1995): 87.

8. J. Cliffone, "Suicide Prevention: A Classroom Presentation to Adolescents," *Social Work* 38 (1993): 197–203; L. L. Eggert, E. A. Thompson, J. R. Herting, and L. J. Nicholas, "Reducing Suicide Potential among High-Risk Youth: Tests of a School-based Prevention Program," *Suicide and Life-Threatening Behavior* 25 (1995): 276–96; J. Kalafat and M. Elias, "An Evaluation of Adolescent Suicide Intervention Classes," *Suicide and Life-Threatening Behavior* 24 (1994): 224–33; J. Kalafat and C. Gagliano, "The Use of Simulations to Assess the Impact of an Adolescent Suicide Response Curriculum," *Suicide and Life-Threatening Behavior* 26 (1996): 359–64; I. Orbach and H. Bar-Joseph, "The Impact of a Suicide Prevention Program for Adolescents on Suicidal Tendencies, Hopelessness, Ego Identity, and Coping," *Suicide and Life-Threatening Behavior* 23 (1993): 120–9.

9. J. Kalafat and D. M. Ryerson, "The Implementation and Institutionalization of a School-based Youth Suicide Prevention Program," *Journal of Primary Prevention* 19 (1999): 157–75; F. J. Zenere III, and P. J. Lazarus, "The Decline of Youth Suicidal Behavior in an Urban, Multicultural Public School System Following the Introduction of a Suicide Prevention and Intervention Program," *Suicide and Life-Threatening Behavior* 27 (1997): 387–403.

10. D. Shaffer, P. Fisher, R. H. Hicks, M. Parides, and M. Gould, "Psychiatric Diagnosis in Child and Adolescent Suicide," *Archives of General Psychiatry* 53 (1996): 339–48.

11. D. Brent, "Risk Factors for Adolescent Suicide and Suicidal Behavior: Mental and Substance Abuse Disorders, Family Environmental Factors, and Life-Stress," *Suicide and Life-Threatening Behavior* 25 (1995): 52–63.

12. M. Gould, P. Fisher, M. Parides, M. Flory, and D. Shaffer, "Psychosocial Risk Factors of Adolescent Completed Suicide," *Archives of General Psychiatry* 53 (1996): 1155–62.

13. P. Lewinson, P. Rohde, and J. Seely, "Adolescent Suicide Ideation and Attempts: Prevalence, Risk Factors and Clinical Implications," *Clinical Psychology Journal and Practice* 3, no. 1 (1996): 25–26.

Part 1: Administrative Readiness Consultation

1. Cheryl DiCara, Susan O'Halloran, and Linda Williams, *Youth Suicide Prevention Intervention and Postvention Guidelines: A Resource for School Personnel*, 3rd ed. (Maine Youth Suicide Prevention Program, 2006).

2. Joint Committee on National Health Education Standards, *National Health Education Standards*, 2nd ed. (American Cancer Society, 2007).

3. R. F. Catalano and J. D. Hawkins, "The Social Development Model: A Theory of Antisocial Behavior," in *Delinquency and Crime: Current Theories*, ed. J. D. Hawkins, 149–97

(New York: Cambridge University Press, 1996); R. F. Catalano, J. D. Hawkins, and M. W. Arthur, "Promoting Science-based Prevention in Communities," *Addictive Behaviors* 27, no. 66 (2002): 951–76; R. F. Catalano and J. D. Hawkins, Response from authors to comments on "Positive Youth Development in the United States: Research Findings on Evaluations on Positive Youth Development Programs," *Prevention and Treatment* 5 (2002): article 20.

Part 2: Training for School Faculty and Staff

1. American Association of Suicidology Web site, www.suicidology.org. Accessed 2009. Use this site to update statistics as necessary.

2. Ernest L. Boyer, *The Basic School: A Community for Learning* (Princeton, NJ: The Carnegie Foundation for the Advancement of Teaching, 1995).

3. This information is adapted from material developed by Edwin Shneidman, *Definition of Suicide* (New York: Wiley, 1985).

4. J. Grossman, J. Hirsch, D. Goldenberg, S. Libby, M. Fendrich, M. Mackesy-Amiti, C. Mazur, and G. Chance, "Strategies for School-based Response to Loss: Proactive Training and Postvention Consultation," *Crisis* 16, no. 1 (1995): 18–26.

Part 3: Parent Workshop

1. American Association of Suicidology Web site, www.suicidology.org. Accessed 2009. Use this site to update statistics as necessary.

2. Ibid.

3. Youth Risk Behavior Survey (Atlanta: Centers for Disease Control and Prevention, 2007).

4. Ernest L. Boyer, *The Basic School: A Community for Learning* (Princeton, NJ: The Carnegie Foundation for the Advancement of Teaching, 1995).

Part 4: Student Curriculum

1. Joint Committee on National Health Education Standards, *National Health Education Standards*, 2nd ed. (American Cancer Society, 2007).

2. This three-step intervention model is used with permission of the Youth Suicide Prevention Program, Seattle, WA.

School-based Suicide Prevention Resources

....

General Resources

American Association of Suicidology. *Guidelines for School-based Suicide Prevention Programs,* 1999. Available on the AAS Web site: www.suicidology.org.

Berman, A. L., and D. A. Jobes. *Adolescent Suicide: Assessment and Intervention.* Washington, DC: American Psychological Association, 1991.

Canter, A. S., and S. A. Carroll, eds. *Crisis Prevention & Response: A Collection of NASP Resources.* Bethesda, MD: National Association of School Psychologists, 1999.

Centers for Disease Control and Prevention. "Suicide Contagion and the Reporting of Suicide: Recommendations from a National Workshop," *Morbidity and Mortality Weekly Report* 43, no. RR-6 (1994): 13–18.

Cobain, B. *When Nothing Matters Anymore: A Survival Guide for Depressed Teens.* Minneapolis: Free Spirit Publishing, 1998.

Davis, J. M., and J. Sandoval. *Suicidal Youth: School-based Intervention and Prevention.* San Francisco: Jossey-Bass, 1991.

Kalafat, J. "The Prevention of Youth Suicide." In *Healthy Children 2010: Enhancing Children's Wellness,* edited by R. P. Weissberg, T. P. Gullotta, B. A. Ryan, and G. R. Adams, 175–213. Thousand Oaks, CA: Sage, 1997.

———."School Approaches to Youth Suicide," *American Behavioral Scientist* 46, no. 9 (2003): 1211–23.

Maine Youth Suicide Prevention Program. www.maine.gov/suicide.

Poland, S. *Suicide Intervention in the Schools.* New York: Guilford Press, 1989.

Ramsay, R. F., B. L. Tanney, R. J. Tierney, and W. A. Lang. *Suicide Intervention Handbook.* Calgary, AB: LivingWorks Education Inc., 1994.

Smith, J. *School Crisis Management Manual: Guidelines for Administrators.* Holmes Beach, FL: Learning Publications, 1997.

Comprehensive Packaged School Community Suicide Prevention Programs

Eastgard, S. *Youth Suicide Prevention Program Toolkit.* Seattle: Youth Suicide Prevention Program, 2000. www.yspp.org

Ryerson, D. *Safe: Teen.* 2002. Available from dianeryerson@aol.com. www.endsuicide.org

127

School-based Suicide Prevention Resources
....

128

Evaluation of School-based Programs

Cliffone, J. "Suicide Prevention: A Classroom Presentation to Adolescents," *Social Work* 38 (1993): 196–203.

Kalafat, J., and M. Elias. "An Evaluation of Adolescent Suicide Intervention Classes," *Suicide and Life-Threatening Behavior* 24 (1994): 224–33.

Kalafat, J., and C. Gagliano. "The Use of Simulations to Assess the Impact of an Adolescent Suicide Response Curriculum," *Suicide and Life-Threatening Behavior* 26 (1996): 359–64.

Kalafat, J., and D. M. Ryerson. "The Implementation and Institutionalization of a School-based Youth Suicide Prevention Program," *Journal of Primary Prevention* 19 (1999): 157–75.

Randell, B. P., L. L. Eggert, and K. C. Pike. "Immediate Post-intervention Effects of Two Brief Youth Suicide Prevention Interventions," *Suicide and Life-Threatening Behavior* 31 (2001): 41–61.

Thompson, E. A., L. L. Eggert, B. P. Randell, and K. C. Pike. "Evaluation of Indicated Suicide Risk Prevention Approaches for Potential High School Dropouts," *American Journal of Public Health* 91 (2001): 742–52.

Zenere, F. J., III, and P. J. Lazarus. "The Decline of Youth Suicidal Behavior in an Urban, Multicultural Public School System Following the Introduction of a Suicide Prevention and Intervention Program," *Suicide and Life-Threatening Behavior* 27 (1997): 387–403.

Postvention Resources

American Association of Suicidology. *Suicide Postvention Guidelines: Suggestions for Dealing with the Aftermath of Suicide in the Schools.* 1998.

Brock, S. E., P. J. Lazarus, and S. R. Jimerson, eds. *Best Practices in School Crisis Prevention and Intervention.* Bethesda, MD: National Association of School Psychologists, 2002.

Brock, S. E., J. Sandoval, and S. Lewis. *Preparing for Crises in Schools.* New York: Wiley, 2001.

DiCara, C., and S. O'Halloran, eds. *Youth Suicide Prevention, Intervention, and Postvention Guidelines: A Resource for School Personnel,* 2006. Available from Maine Youth Suicide Prevention Program (1-800-698-3624 or www.maine.gov/suicide).

Grossman, J. *Team Up to Save Lives: What Your School Should Know about Preventing Youth Suicide,* 1996. CD-ROM available from McDonald's Resource Center (1-800-627-7646).

National Institute for Trauma and Loss in Children. *School Memorials: Should We? How Should We?* Available at www.tlcinstitute.org/Memorials.html.

Underwood, M. M., and K. Dunne-Maxim. *Managing Sudden Traumatic Loss in the Schools.* Washington, DC: American Association of Suicidology, 1997.

Videos

For a list of videos recommended by the American Association of Suicidology see www.suicidology .org/web/guest/stats-and-tools/videos.

Depression: On the Edge (#429). Produced by In the Mix, 114 East 32nd Street #903, New York, NY 10016; 1-800-597-9448 or 212-684-3940.

Fatal Mistakes: Families Shattered by Suicide. Produced by American Foundation for Suicide Prevention, 120 Wall Street, 22nd Floor, New York, NY 10005; 212-363-3500.

Making Educators Partners in Suicide Prevention. Produced by the Society for the Prevention of Teen Suicide, P.O. Box 6835, Freehold, NJ 07728. Available online at www.sptsnj.org.

Not My Kid: Helping Parents Understand Teen Suicide Risk. Produced by the Society for the Prevention of Teen Suicide, P.O. Box 6835, Freehold, NJ 07728. Available online at www.sptsnj.org.

A Preventable Tragedy: First Response to Suicidal Youth. Produced by Center for Educational Media, Portland, Maine, for the Maine Youth Suicide Prevention Program.

About the Authors

....

Maureen Underwood, L.C.S.W.

Maureen Underwood is a licensed clinical social worker and certified group psychotherapist with over thirty-five years of experience in mental health and crisis intervention. From 1985 to 2000, she was the coordinator of the New Jersey Adolescent Suicide Prevention Project. In this role, she initiated collaborative relationships between mental health and educational systems, provided inservice training, provided consultation on policy development, and assisted in the implementation of procedures for school-based crisis management. In addition to her other numerous publications, Maureen is the co-author of *Managing Sudden Traumatic Loss in the Schools* and the author of the National Association of Social Work's policy statement on adolescent suicide. In her current role as the clinical director of the Society for the Prevention of Teen Suicide, Maureen has developed a series of online videos and resources for educators, parents, and students in youth suicide prevention.

John Kalafat, Ph.D.

John Kalafat was a pioneer in community psychology. He was an internationally recognized expert in youth suicide prevention and crisis intervention who consulted with state, national, and overseas organizations. From co-founding a crisis counseling center to authoring books on youth suicide and divorce, John was at the forefront of his field. His most recent publication of crisis-line evaluation has been central in guiding the National Suicide Prevention Lifeline. John was past president of the American Association of Suicidology, a fellow in the Society for Community Research & Action and Psychotherapy divisions of the American Psychological Association, and a professor in the Rutgers Graduate School of Applied and Professional Psychology. His career spanned forty years and embodied the "scientist-practitioner" model: his passion for research was driven by his love for getting directly involved with those who intervene with individuals in crisis. John, who passed away in late October 2007, has left a global legacy and a model for all of us to follow.

The Maine Youth Suicide Prevention Program

The Maine Youth Suicide Prevention Program (MYSPP) is a multi-agency effort coordinated by the Injury Prevention Program in the Maine Center for Disease Control and Prevention (Maine CDC) in the state's Department of Health and Human Services. The long-term goal of the MYSPP is to reduce the incidence of fatal and non-fatal suicidal behavior